D0611230

Studies in Sir THOMAS BROWNE

R: White sculpsit:

The true Effigies of
S^r THO: BROWN *of Norwich* K^t
M.D.

*

Studies in

Sir THOMAS
BROWNE

*

by **ROBERT RALSTON CAWLEY** *and* **GEORGE YOST**

University of Oregon UBooks

EUGENE, OREGON

1965

PR 3327
.C3

Copyright © 1965 University of Oregon

TO

MARGARET ELIZABETH CAWLEY

and

RUTH SHEPHARD YOST

*

208458

*

Preface

*

I N THE PAST FEW DECADES criticism of the works of Sir Thomas Browne has taken a gratifying turn. After an extended
period during which essayists wrote freely of the charms
of Sir Thomas' famous style, critics came to see that underlying that style was more thought than had been recognized.
Some significance may be attached to the fact that for over two
centuries certain chronological inaccuracies in the widely read
conclusion to *The Garden of Cyrus* went undetected. This tendency to underestimate Browne's intellectual capacity is the
more extraordinary when we consider his many contacts with
the outstanding minds of his day; what impresses any student
of Browne is the number of specialists who acknowledge him as
an authority. It makes, however, for an even greater satisfaction
to see the tide now setting strongly in the opposite direction.
A good example of this healthful tendency is to be observed in
Professor Jeremiah S. Finch's corrective book, *Sir Thomas
Browne: A Doctor's Life of Science and Faith* (1950).

It is hoped that the three studies contained in this volume
may contribute something to the recent drift. The first study
aims to show that the longest, and most neglected, of all
Browne's works, *Pseudodoxia epidemica*, was in its time a book
quite definitely to be reckoned with. In fact, instead of its being,
as some misguided critics have tried to make out, a book full of
outmoded material, it was a study seriously needed in its age to
offset beliefs held even by many of the intelligentsia.

The purpose of the second study is to estimate the impact of Aristotle's mind upon Browne's. A complete examination of this important influence has never previously been undertaken. Obviously it is crucial for any full understanding of the Norwich doctor that his relationship with the great Greek philosopher should be thoroughly investigated. And, what in its way is just as important, one can clearly follow Aristotle's changing reputation as seen in the mirror of Browne's mind.

The third and last study also concerns itself primarily with Sir Thomas' thought. Here we can observe the kind of books to which he naturally turned as well as the particular use he made of them in developing his own ideas. There is nothing more characteristic of the man than the selective process by which he chose to emphasize certain passages in his authors so that he could construct theories that he hoped would stand the test of time.

We wish to thank Professor Kester Svendsen, head of the English Department at the University of Oregon, for having read the whole book in manuscript and for having made valuable suggestions. We wish also to thank Professor Whitney J. Oates, formerly chairman of the Classics Department at Princeton, for checking the parts of Professor Yost's study that have specifically to do with the classical *languages*. The officers of the Modern Language Association graciously permitted the reprinting (with some revisions) of Professor Cawley's article, "Sir Thomas Browne and His Reading."

Finally, we acknowledge with deep gratitude the financial assistance granted by the Princeton University Committee on Research in the Humanities and Social Sciences.

Frank Livingstone Huntley's interesting book, *Sir Thomas Browne, a Biographical and Critical Study*, appeared after the present book was accepted for publication.

R.R.C.

G.Y.

June 1965

*

Contents

*

ix

*

The Timeliness of
Pseudodoxia Epidemica

*

A RECENT CRITIC, writing of Sir Thomas Browne, has said that "since the beginning of the nineteenth century criticism has been literary rather than philosophical."[1] For this regrettable circumstance the Romantics must bear the blame, though, it should be confessed, misinterpretation of what they wrote on the part of their successors makes the latter almost as culpable. Paradoxical as it may seem, Sir Thomas' famed style has done his reputation a great disservice. "The value of Browne," wrote another critic in 1915, "now lies wholly in his style"![2] This approach has turned men's minds away from his longest and most ambitious work, *Pseudodoxia epidemica*, and towards *Urn Burial* and *The Garden of Cyrus*. For writers of this school of thought, *Pseudodoxia* becomes inevitably a catchall of unconsidered trifles. Sir Thomas himself, I feel sure, would have been deeply distressed over this

---

[1] Geoffrey Keynes, *A Bibliography of Sir Thomas Browne* (Cambridge, 1924), p. 141.

[2] Hugh Walker, *The English Essay and Essayists* (London, 1915), p. 79. The tenor of much nineteenth-century criticism may be judged from Pater's statement that many take *Pseudodoxia* to be "a serious refutation of fairy tales." *MacMillan's Magazine*, LIV (1886), 13. For a continuation of this attitude in the present century, cf. W. P. Dunn's *Sir Thomas Browne, A Study in Religious Philosophy* (2nd ed.; Minneapolis, 1950), p. 16: "That inchoate mass of half-scholastic erudition which goes by the name of *Vulgar Errors* is largely a curiosity and a work of entertainment rather than instruction."

I

wrong emphasis. Generally speaking, it is only in the eddies of criticism that we get the balance partially restored. "The 'Vulgar Errors' is an invaluable help to the student of scientific thought in the seventeenth century."[3] It is true that no separate English edition of *Pseudodoxia* appeared after 1672. But in France, where perhaps ideas were stirring even more actively, the work was kept very much alive.[4] "A prophet hath honor save." Fortunately, for the past quarter century scholars have perceived the injustice and have made efforts to set the balance right.[5] "It is well known by now," wrote Professor Alwin Thaler in 1931, "that most of this exception against Browne [Walter Pater's] (specifically, that he was as much an antiquary as a scientist) is valid only as it applies to virtually all thinking men of his time, including, to some extent, Francis Bacon himself."[6] Perhaps the

---

[3] W. A. Nicholson, "Sir Thomas Browne as a Naturalist," in *Transactions of the Norfolk and Norwich Naturalists' Society* (Norwich, 1904), VII, 74. Nicholson says further: " 'Vulgar Errors' was written for men of education, by one, and so affords a good index of the way in which natural phenomena were viewed at that period" (*ibid.*). Again and again Nicholson calls attention to Browne's conscientious accuracy. Cf. pp. 77, 79, 81, 82, 86.

E. S. Merton, "Sir Thomas Browne's Scientific Quest," *Journal of the History of Medicine*, III (1948), 214-228, makes an important contribution in this connection: "Although Browne refers to 'the three Determinators of Truth, Authority, Sense, and Reason', and although he certainly depends upon authority in practice, his more usual references are to experience and reason alone as the guides to truth" (p. 220). Merton also draws some interesting distinctions between Bacon's "idols" and Browne's causes of human error. See especially pp. 215-220. See also Merton's interesting study of Browne's botany, "The Botany of Sir Thomas Browne," *Isis*, XLVII (1956), 161-171.

[4] See list of eighteenth-century editions given in Geoffrey Keynes, *Bibliography*, pp. 61 ff.; and Olivier Leroy, *A French Bibliography of Sir Thomas Browne* (London, 1931). Cf. also the statement by Morhof, talking about errors in natural history: "Hoc in argumento nemo plenius inter recentiores versatus est, quam *Thomas Browne*, Anglus, Autor illius libri, qui inscribitur: *Religio Medici*. Is patria lingua librum scripsit hoc Titulo: *Pseudodoxia Epidemica*; doctum sane et elegantem." Daniel G. Morhof, *Polyhistor*, 3 vols. (Lübeck, 1747), II, 131. Morhof wrote also: "Multa sunt in illo libro [*Pseudodoxia*] notatu dignissima." *Ibid.*, I, 404. For Browne's continental reputation in general, see *Sir Thomas Browne's Works, Including His Life and Correspondence*, ed. Simon Wilkin, 4 vols. (London, 1835-36), I, lxv ff.

[5] Cf. Almonte C. Howell's "Sir Thomas Browne and Seventeenth-Century Scientific Thought," *Studies in Philology*, XXII, 61-80.

[6] "Sir Thomas Browne and the Elizabethans," *Studies in Philology*, XXVIII (1931), 104. Cf. also Gordon K. Chalmers, "Sir Thomas Browne, True Scientist," *Osiris*, II (1936), 28-79. See especially pp. 28-32 and 69: "Thus

time has come to examine *Pseudodoxia* in detail with the purpose of showing how far these later critics are justified in their general statements.

First, however, it is necessary to make some study of the conditions under which Browne was writing in order to sense the special preoccupations of his generation so far as scientific thought went.[7] Certainly the age was no different from others in the tenacity with which it held to old beliefs. Bacon's idols of the cave and theater persisted. The great struggle between Ancients and Moderns was already moving towards its last phase. And the very fact that the Moderns so insisted on being heard made adherents of the old argue their view all the more vigorously. Like Bacon, therefore, Browne found himself in the ironic position of having to oppose the very Ancients whom he admired.[8] Then, too, he was confronted with a broadly human tendency; he would "only desire men would not swallow dubiosities for certainties, and receive as principles points mainly controvertible."[9] The poets were to blame here for they perpetuated myths as truths, for their own purposes retelling disproved legends and thus deceiving immature minds. From our position we can scarcely estimate the amount of misinformation dispensed and confirmed by a phenomenally popular work like Du Bartas' *His Divine Weekes and Workes*.[10] Only in our own

in the time of its formation Sir Thomas Browne participated in the modern idea of scientific progress." Dewey K. Ziegler, *In Divided and Distinguished Worlds: Religion and Rhetoric in the Writings of Sir Thomas Browne* (Cambridge, Mass., 1943) is right in maintaining that G. K. Chalmers' unpublished Harvard thesis (1933) proves "conclusively Browne's familiarity with the most advanced science of his time" (p. 104). Note also Browne's own statement in a letter (December 23, 1668) to his son Edward: "I keepe the sheets of the Transactions [of the Royal Society] as they come out, monethly." *Works*, ed. Wilkin, I, 169.

[7] For Dr. Paul H. Kocher's analysis of the relation between science and religion in the preceding century, see page 119 *infra*.

[8] He deplored, as he says, "the dictates of antiquity." Cf. also *The Works of Sir Thomas Browne*, ed. Geoffrey Keynes, 6 vols. (London, 1928-31), II, 50: "Having thus totally relinquisht them [the Ancients] in some things, it may not be presumtuous, to examine them in others; but surely most unreasonable to adhere to them in all, as though they were infallible, or could not err in any."

[9] *Works*, ed. Wilkin, III, 235.

[10] This is to be seen, for one place, in the monumental edition of *The Works of Du Bartas*, ed. U. T. Holmes, Jr., J. C. Lyons, and R. W. Linker,

century has the extent of that influence been realized. Among other poetic utterances, Hamlet alone gave expression to a dozen such myths as the chameleon feeding on air and the pigeon lacking gall. And, when we transcend the bounds of poetry, Pliny's *Natural History*,[11] especially in Philemon Holland's translation, which Browne held accountable for three-fourths of the lies passing current, must have exercised a determining influence beyond our modern comprehension. As for the Middle Ages, Bartholomew's *De proprietatibus rerum*, dating from the thirteenth century, when books were comparatively few, and those few regarded as encyclopedic authorities, still held unexampled sway. Professor Kester Svendsen, in his discerning book *Milton and Science*,[12] has done much to show how fables persisted through such medieval compilations, which were widely read and devoutly followed. Still another factor was the common proverb; we cannot, for instance, realize the effect on the populace of sayings like "as shapeless as an unlicked cub." And, finally, there were the pictures, which were so popular in Browne's day and before. Sir Thomas was fully aware of the part they played in perpetuating outworn creeds; and he was himself addicted to their study, poring over them for hours at a time while the quincunx of heaven ran low.[13] He complained even of the graphic

---

3 vols. (Chapel Hill, 1935-40). This work contains a summary (III, 537-542) of the unpublished dissertation of William R. Abbot, "Studies in the Influence of Du Bartas in England, 1584-1641" (University of North Carolina, 1931). There is also G. C. Taylor's *Milton's Use of Du Bartas* (Cambridge, Mass., 1934).

11 His was the first scientific classic to see print (Venice, 1469); and Holland's popular translation (London, 1601) was the second work of ancient science to appear in English.

12 Cambridge, Mass., 1956. See especially, in the realm of natural history, his fifth chapter, "All the Beasts of the Earth: The Animal Kingdom in Milton." Besides the prominence he gives to Bartholomew, he treats Isidore of Seville, the *Physiologus*, *L'Image du Monde*, and Alexander Neckam's *De naturis rerum*. These medieval encyclopedias are considered by Louis Wright in chapter 15 of *Middle Class Culture in Elizabethan England* (Chapel Hill, 1935). See the section on animal lore, pp. 571-574. Of the Renaissance encyclopedists, Svendsen has John Maplet's *A Greene Forest* (London, 1567), Pierre de La Primaudaye's *The French Academie* (London, 1618), and John Swan's *Speculum mundi* (Cambridge, 1635).

13 It will be recalled that he devoted most of one whole book (V) of *Pseudodoxia* to "pictures." For Browne's addiction to hieroglyphics, see Gordon K. Chalmers, "Hieroglyphs and Sir Thomas Browne," *Virginia Quarterly Review*, XI (1935), 547-560.

qualities of hieroglyphics in setting impressions that were erroneous.[14] John Guillim's *A Display of Heraldrie*,[15] with its mythical menagerie engraved as armorial bearings, would thus become a kind of seventeenth-century hieroglyphic, at least in part performing the same function. Still another circumstance should not be overlooked; men of considerable standing in Browne's time believed implicitly in many of the very things he was trying to refute. The Southampton schoolmaster Alexander Ross is a good example.[16] Ross's reputation has suffered grievously at the hands of the Brownophile, Simon Wilkin. It is true that, in his attacks on Sir Thomas in the *Medicus medicatus* (London, 1645) and the *Arcana microcosmi* (London, 1652), he was traditional and conservative. But he was probably not more so than the average intelligent "Ancient" of the time. Certainly Ross had his following. His *Pansebeia* (London, 1653) went through six editions in the seventeenth century, and the list it contains of his twenty-seven publications is impressive enough.

All these matters considered, we can think of Sir Thomas as being confronted with a colossus of entrenched beliefs. And the more we contemplate his age, the greater appears the need for such a book as *Pseudodoxia*, which appeared first in 1646. Symonds' contention, therefore, that Browne "wasted ingenuity and patience upon subjects of little interest"[17] may be regarded as

---

[14] Cf. *Works*, ed. Wilkin, III, 149.

[15] Fourth ed., London, 1660.

[16] I hope soon to publish a study of Ross's position in his century. He was clearly not what Wilkin and the famous distich in *Hudibras* make him out to be. If he was under the spell of what he called "Aristotle's pure fountains," so were most of the intellectuals of his time. And his final caution to Browne was sufficiently moderate: "an Admonition not to sleight the Ancients opinion and Doctrine." *Arcana microcosmi* (London, 1652), p. 201. The man who wrote in 1651 that "all is not Witchcraft which is so called" (*ibid.*, pp. 120-121) may hardly be charged with mental apathy. And the reader who comes fresh from Wilkin's contemptuous scoffings may be surprised to find the following in *Arcana*: "I acknowledge there is much worth...in your Book [*Pseudodoxia*]; and, because you are so ingenuous and modest as to disclaime these opinions if they square not with maturer judgments, I have with as great modesty and gentlenesse as I could, refelled them, having neither dipt my pen in *gall*, nor mingled my inke with *vinegar*. The God of truth direct all our hearts into the way of truth" (p. 115).

[17] *Religio medici*, ed. J. A. Symonds, Camelot Classics (London, 1886), Introduction. Even an essay like Sir Leslie Stephen's in *Hours in a Library*,

exactly the opposite to the truth. Against the nineteenth-century assumption that Browne's longest work may safely be disregarded stands the evidence of a near-contemporary authority: "This Work met with a general Reception."[18] Readers have only to turn to Blount's *Natural History*[19] to observe the standing Browne's book had in his own century, and to John Brand's *Observations on Popular Antiquities*[20] to see how it was regarded in the century that followed. So far, therefore, as we can ever hope to penetrate the inner sanctum of Browne's fascinating mind, we might say that he reasoned somewhat after this fashion: there exists around us a solid wall of superstition and mythology; the scientific books of our day are doing what they can to make breaches in that wall, though they themselves are unconsciously purveying their fair share of untruths; perhaps I can do something to dispel the mists of error by writing a book that possibly will be more widely read than the scientific treatises. This, as I

3 vols. (London, 1892), I, 269-299, for all its good intentions, has done much harm. Similarly, Olivier Leroy in *Le Chevalier Thomas Browne: Médecin, Styliste et Métaphysicien* (Paris, 1931), in his fifth chapter, "Le Savant et L'Erudit," while trying to be fair, cannot avoid a condescending attitude towards Browne as scientist. He does say (p. 200) that such men as Pascal and Descartes held to some of the same beliefs.

18 *Posthumous Works of the Learned Sir Thomas Browne, Kt.* (London, 1712), p. v.

19 Thomas Pope Blount, *A Natural History Containing Many Not Common Observations Extracted out of the Best Modern Writers* (London, 1693). Cf., for example, pp. 27, 29, 45, 58, et passim. For instance, on the nature of the glowworm's light, Browne is cited (p. 313) as the final authority.

20 Newcastle upon Tyne, 1777. Actually Brand lived on into the nineteenth century. The following is typical: "Doctor Browne leaves me little more on this Subject [origin of the expression "under the rose"], than the easy and agreeable Task of making him speak concisely and in *plain English*" (p. 366). He then proceeds to reproduce Browne (*Works*, ed. Keynes, III, 144) almost word for word.

We should note further what the great ornithologist Francis Willughby says of him; citing Browne as authority for his description of the stork, he goes on: "My honoured Friend Sir Thomas Brown of Norwich, a person deservedly famous, for his skill in all parts of learning, but especially in natural History, sent me a picture of one of these birds taken on the Coast of Norfolk, drawn by the life, with a short description of it." *Ornithology* (London, 1678), p. 286.

It is especially significant that the scholar who made the corrections in ink in the Bodleian copy of Willughby is constantly citing or quoting Browne as authority. Cf. pp. 146, 180, 282, 357, et passim.

say, may have been the way Sir Thomas' thoughts ran. So help me, I can see no other explanation for the elaborate system of commonplace books we know he was keeping in the ten years between 1635 and 1645.

Critics have further maintained that *Pseudodoxia* is a collection of *disjecta membra*. Here Coleridge, in one of those strokes of genius, is nearer right when he refers to "his entireness in every subject."[21] Read carefully, Browne's work shows a remarkable consistency in its approach. Clearly he aimed to take up each subject with an open mind, explore its possibilities, examine its authorities, test it by reason and experience, and render some decision.[22] Perhaps what has misled some readers is that they have not perceived that an important part of his purpose was the justifying of certain truths that others had set down as errors. In this effort he customarily used the best information available to him or his century. And he had enough of Bacon in him to be unwilling to discard a theory until evidence had proved it wrong.

Perhaps nothing has been more often alleged against this side of Browne than his experiments to test the belief that a suspended kingfisher will infallibly reveal the wind's direction.[23] It will be remembered that he calls it "a conceit supported chiefly by present practice, yet not made out by Reason or Experience."[24] That it was not entirely useless for him to prove this by experiment may be seen in a statement by so widely accepted an authority as the ornithologist Francis Willughby: "It is a Vulgar persuasion, that this bird, being hung up on an untwisted thread by the Bill in any room, will turn its Breast to that quarter of the Heaven whence the wind blows: They that doubt of it may try

---

[21] *Literary Remains of Samuel Taylor Coleridge*, ed. H. N. Coleridge, 2 vols. (London, 1836-39), II, 414.

[22] Among others, Browne has two important statements of his objectives. In one place (*Works*, ed. Wilkin, II, 408), he speaks of the "three determinators of truth—authority, sense, and reason." And in another (*ibid.*, p. 534) of "the two great pillars of truth, experience and solid reason." Cf. also *The Garden of Cyrus* (*Works*, ed. Keynes, IV, 124), where Browne refers to "sense and ocular Observation, which seems to me the surest path, to trace the Labyrinth of truth."

[23] See *Works*, ed. Keynes, II, 213-216.

[24] *Works*, ed. Keynes, II, 213.

it."[25] And Robert Lovell, in a work that appeared years after *Pseudodoxia*, vouched for the same: "Some say that their *breast* alwayes turneth to the *wind*, being hung up by the bill with a thred, in the house."[26] Lovell was an Oxford graduate, a doctor with a successful medical practice. His book significantly omits many of the misconceptions still generally held and, being a medical treatise, it obviously makes every effort to be scientifically accurate. He had read widely and experimented freely. But this is not the whole story. In the same year in which Lovell's book was published, the august Royal Society was talking about "the fish, which turns to the wind, when suspended by a thread." The observation is solemnly recorded in the minutes of the Society for March 25, 1661, fifteen years at least after Sir Thomas had made his experiments.[27]

Browne questioned many other theories for which the Royal Society later stood sponsor. While we are in the realm of natural history (and, indeed, with Browne's great interest in the subject, we shall have to spend much of our time there), we might mention that mysterious creature, the salamander. "That a Salamander," wrote Browne, "is able to live in flames, to endure and put out fire, is an assertion, not only of great antiquity, but confirmed by frequent, and not contemptible testimony. . . . All which notwithstanding, there is on the negative, Authority

---

[25] *Ornithology* (London, 1678), p. 146. Note that the date (1678) is thirty-two years after the publication of *Pseudodoxia*. In the Bodleian copy of this book, some later scholar has written in ink Browne's refutation.

[26] *A Compleat History of Animals and Minerals*, 2 vols. in one (Oxford, 1661), I, 158. Thomas Lupton tells the same story, maintaining that the kingfisher, "beeing hanged up in the ayre by the necke, his neb or bill will be alwaies directe or straight against the winde. This was tolde mee for a verie trueth, by one that knew it by proofe." *A Thousand Notable Things of Sundrie Sorts* (London, 1595), p. 213.

[27] Thomas Birch, *The History of the Royal Society*, 4 vols. (London, 1756), I, 19. It should be remembered that the Royal Society did not even get its charter until 1662, sixteen years after the publication of *Pseudodoxia*. Cf. Kent's diatribe against Oswald:

"Such smiling rogues . . .

. . . .

. . . turn their halcyon beaks

With every gale and vary of their masters, . . ."

Lear, II, ii, 79-85

A handsome edition of Thomas Sprat's *History of the Royal Society* was issued at Washington University, St. Louis, in 1958.

and Experience . . . "[28] Twenty years later Dr. Croune reported to the Royal Society on a salamander owned by the Great Duke of Florence that was cast into the fire, which it promptly put out, "and then seemed to lie there quietly."[29] This so impressed the Society that the members decided forthwith to do some experimenting themselves. They may or may not have known the views on the subject of the traveler Sir Thomas Herbert, who described the Madagascar salamander as being "extreme cold by nature, whence (like ice) for some time they endure the fire, yea (if little) extinguish it as Aristotle affirms."[30] But they surely did know that Aristotle had affirmed the belief,[31] and they knew too that Bacon had lent it the sanction of his majestic name. He says: "There is an ancient received tradition of the salamander, that it liveth in the fire, and hath force also to extinguish the fire."[32] And then he proceeds on his own to allow the possibility and offer his rational explanation of how it might be.[33] Edward Topsell, who was accepted by many in Browne's time as the foremost authority on natural history, weighs the whole matter carefully and concludes that, because of the hardness and "thicknesse of the skin, and cold constitution," it manages to survive in fire longer than most animals.[34] That sort of rationalization, all too rare, made Browne's task easier.

---

[28] *Works*, ed. Keynes, II, 231.
[29] Birch, *The History of the Royal Society*, II, 100. Entry for June 27, 1666. The entry continues: "This [Dr. Croune's account] was confirmed by Mr. Boyle and Mr. Willughby, as to other salamanders; and the latter of these two having proposed, that whereas the water-newt seems to be *salamandra aquatica*, some of them might be provided against the next meeting, to try what they would do, when cast into the fire."
[30] *Some Yeares Travels* (London, 1677), p. 23.
[31] *Aristotle's History of Animals*, trans. Richard Cresswell (London, 1862), p. 126.
[32] *The Works of Francis Bacon*, ed. Spedding, Ellis, and Heath, 14 vols. (London, 1857-74), II, 626 (in "Experiment solitary touching the salamander").
[33] Samuel Bochart goes further: "Ex igne generatur animal salamandra nomine, quod solo igne alitur: quin ignis est materia eius, et fit in fornacibus vitri, quae arserunt per septem annos." *Hierozoicon, sive bipertitum opus de animalibus s. scripturae* (Frankfurt, 1675), Pt. II, p. 824.
[34] Edward Topsell, *The History of Four-footed Beasts and Serpents* (London, 1658), pp. 747-750. This work includes two earlier books by Topsell: *The Historie of Foure-footed Beastes* (London, 1607) and *The History of*

In the section on the "Tainct," we find a good example of what Sir Thomas' critics have chosen to call his unwarrantable credulity. "There is found in the Summer," writes Browne,

a kind of Spider called a Tainct, of a red colour, and so little of body that ten of the largest will hardly outway a grain; this by Country people is accounted a deadly poison unto Cows and Horses; who, if they suddenly die, and swell thereon, ascribe their death hereto, . . . Now to satisfie the doubts of men we have called this tradition unto experiment; we have given hereof unto Dogs, Chickens, Calves and Horses, . . . ; yet never could find the least disturbance ensue.[35]

But he was disinclined to reject the underlying principle.

For that a poison cannot destroy in so small a bulk; we have no reason to affirm. For if as Leo Africanus reporteth, the tenth part of a grain of the poison of Nubia [in marginal note, "*granum Nubiae*"], will dispatch a man in two hours . . . ; we cannot as impossible reject this way of destruction; or deny the power of death in so narrow a circumscription.[36]

Twenty years after Sir Thomas performed his experiment, the Royal Society recorded the following in its minutes:

Blount produced a little red spider no bigger than a pin's head, commonly called a *Taint*, which, it was said, would kill a cow or ox by swelling them extremely, if it be taken down into the belly. . . . Dr. Charlton mentioned, that it was not probable, that the little spider should be the cause of the death of oxen and cows. . . . It was ordered, that some of these *Taints* should be procured by the operator, to try, whether they would kill a dog or cat.[37]

Four years later Henry Howard, who had been appointed ambassador "to the emperor Tafiletta," was commissioned by the Society to verify "whether *granum Nubiae* will kill in a less quantity than any other known poison."[38] It is impossible, of course, now to determine how far a popular book like Topsell's *The History of Serpents* was responsible for setting the wide-

---

Serpents (London, 1608), and Thomas Moffett's *The Theater of Insects* (London, 1634). Unless otherwise specified, all references will be to the 1658 edition.

[35] *Works*, ed. Keynes, II, 298-299. Cf. "Lycidas," ll. 45-46:
    "As killing as the . . .
    . . . taint-worm to the weanling Herds that graze."

[36] *Works*, ed. Keynes, II, 299.

[37] Birch, *The History of the Royal Society*, II, 28. Entry for March 29, 1665.

[38] Birch, *op. cit.*, II, 374. Entry for May 27, 1669.

spread belief that "all Spiders are venomous, but yet some more, and some lesse."[39] And Topsell goes on to say that there are to be found "in Harvesttime" "certain small Spiders," "of a very red and fiery colour, such as we Englishmen call Twinges, by eating or licking up of which, both Oxen and other Beasts do many times die."[40] There was indeed but one country where spiders' poison was not effective: "It hath bene reported, that in Ireland be many spiders, and some verye great, and that being eaten of the Irishmen, have not performed any shewe of venime: *it may be, that the greater poyson subdueth the lesse.*"[41]

Concerning reputedly the most deadly of all spiders, the tarantula, a queer theory was commonly held. And here Browne tended to go along:

> Some doubt many have of the Tarantula, or poisonous Spider of Calabria, and that magical cure of the bite thereof by Musick. But since we observe that many attest it from experience: Since the learned Kircherus hath positively averred it, and set down the songs and tunes solemnly used for it; Since some also affirm the Tarantula it self will dance upon certain stroaks, whereby they set their instruments against its poison; we shall not at all question it.[42]

At a meeting of the Royal Society on March 11, 1669, the discussion centered on tarantulas. Some members said that their victims "must dance once a year." Others claimed that different patients required different airs, according to the type of tarantula. Robert Boyle himself was present on this occasion for he added his own testimony.[43] I fear etymology was the bad boy

---

[39] *The History of Serpents* (originally published in 1608), in Topsell, *op. cit.*, p. 769.

[40] *Ibid.*, p. 770.

[41] *Batman uppon Bartholome* (London, 1582), p. 347. In the southern states of America a proper remedy was found. There an especially poisonous variety of spider was turned up, but against its bite "a glass of brandy is stated, however, to produce instant relief." Robert Patterson, *Letters on the Natural History of the Insects Mentioned in Shakespeare's Plays* (London, 1838), pp. 216 ff.

Robert Burton appears to have believed that ague could be cured by wearing a spider hung round the neck in a nutshell. *The Anatomy of Melancholy*, 2 vols. (London, 1837), II, 134. As James E. Harting well says, "When such men are so credulous, how can we wonder at the superstitions of the illiterate?"

[42] *Works*, ed. Keynes, II, 305.

[43] Birch, *The History of the Royal Society*, II, 355.

here because the popular dance the "tarantella" was regularly
connected with "tarantula" since both words were derived from
"Taranto." Towards the end of the century Thomas Pope
Blount brought in the evidence of a friend who had actually seen
the effects in Taranto itself: ". . . amongst the rest a Phisician, on
whom the Tune that fitted his Distemper had the same Operation
as on the other Patients."[44] Moreover, he gave Robert Boyle's
essay on "languid motion"[45] as authority. Similarly, Thomas
Moffett brought forward a whole legion of authorities, "our
most famous, and dear Masters."[46] And Topsell, discussing the
theory at some length, concluded that the tarantula's victims
"are generally delighted with musical Instruments," and that,
"though they be so neer unto death, yet if they hear any
musick, they come again to themselves."[47]

While our ancestors were talking about poisons, they were
naturally led to consider their antidotes. And chief among these
was the unicorn's horn.[48] Browne, in a chapter on the subject,
conceded that there was not one but many unicorns.[49] He
granted even that the unicorn's horn might have some antidotal
quality since similar substances were known to have medicinal
value. "But when we affirm it is not only Antidotal to proper
venoms, . . . but that it resisteth . . . poysons which kill by
second qualities, . . . I doubt we exceed the properties of its
nature, and the promises of experiment will not secure the
adventure."[50]

---

[44] *A Natural History* ... (London, 1693), p. 324.
[45] *An Essay of the Great Effects of Even Languid and Unheeded Motion*
(London, 1685).
[46] *The Theater of Insects*, in Topsell, *op. cit.*, p. 1061. Cf. also Joannes
Jonstonus, *An History of the Wonderful Things of Nature* (London,
1657), p. 263: "For those that are stung with the *Tarantula*, some alwaies
sing." Two of Jonstonus' works on natural history are listed in *A Catalogue
of the Libraries of the Learned Sir Thomas Brown, and Dr. Edward Brown,
His Son* (London, 1711).
[47] *The History of Serpents*, in Topsell, *op. cit.*, p. 772.
[48] A disproportionate amount of Sir Hamon L'Estrange's "Observations on
Pseudodoxia Epidemica" (British Museum MS. Sloan 1839) is devoted to
the unicorn. L'Estrange says (p. 50): "I have lately read over Dr. Brownes
accurate disquisition and enquiries about vulgar Errours ... with singular
pleasure and delight."
[49] *Works*, ed. Keynes, II, 271-277.
[50] *Works*, ed. Keynes, II, 276.

It was natural that the Royal Society should test the effectiveness of what was considered the best antidote against what was considered one of the strongest poisons. And this it did: "A circle was made with powder of unicorn's horn, and a spider set in the middle of it, but it immediately ran out. The trial being repeated several times, the spider once made some stay on the powder."[51] This was on July 24, 1661. And the Society at other times took cognizance of the unicorn. In that same year the Duke of Buckingham promised to bring in a piece of the horn.[52] The following year Mr. Southwell produced a great horn, "said to be an unicorn's."[53] And in the same year an emissary reported to the Society from Bantam (in response to the Society's questions), telling of a specimen of which he personally knew: "If the horn be good, and any filthy or venomous liquor be put in it, you will perceive the water to bubble up with a gentle susurration."[54] Years later the queries were still being made.[55]

In this instance the Ancients were more sinned against than sinning, Aelian standing alone in contending for the horn's "medical vertue." The Bible and the Middle Ages are solely to blame. Even the great Albertus vouched for most of the legends.[56] But probably the most determinative influence in this connection was Topsell, whose book *The History of Four-footed Beasts* was generally accepted as authority until mid-century and probably beyond. He quotes the Bible and concludes, "God himself must needs be traduced, if there be no Unicorn in the world."[57] His whole chapter on the subject is so

---

[51] Birch, *The History of the Royal Society*, I, 35. Cf. Webster's *Vittoria* (Act II):

> "Make of the powder a preservative circle,
>   And in it put a spider."

We should never underestimate the power of drama to purvey misinformation.

[52] Birch, *op. cit.*, I, 26. Entry for June 5, 1661.

[53] *Ibid.*, p. 83. Entry for May 14, 1662.

[54] *Ibid.*, p. 319. John Parkinson testified that "Unicornes Horne likewise is a precious Jewell of high esteeme, and with Princes kept alwayes in their treasury to be used upon occasion for themselves." *Theatrum botanicum: The Theater of Plantes* (London, 1640), p. 1611.

[55] Birch, *op. cit.*, III, 481. Cf. also *ibid.*, II, 53; IV, 31-32.

[56] *Divi Alberti Magni de animalibus* (Venice, 1519), p. 183 verso.

[57] *The History of Four-footed Beasts* (originally published in 1607), in Topsell, *op. cit.*, p. 552.

similar in pattern to Browne's that it is probable that Sir Thomas, in his chapter on the subject, had Topsell's book in mind. Topsell begins by saying that there are actually many unicorns; then he cites a host of authorities, among them contemporaries, and refers to the two horns preserved "at *Venice* in the Treasury of S. *Marks* Church."[58] And Browne in turn speaks of "those two in the treasure of St. Mark."[59] Topsell writes, "In the Temple of *Dennis,* near unto *Paris,* there was a Unicorns horn six foot long."[60] And Browne mentions "that famous one which is preserved at St. Dennis near Paris."[61] Both writers are skeptical, and both arraign apothecaries who "sell a kinde of false adulterated Horn."[62] But Topsell is somewhat like a variorum editor who feels it his duty to put it all in. He tells stories of miraculous cures as if he had himself observed them. "It is," he writes, "more over commended of Physitians of our time against the pestilent feaver, . . . against the bitings of ravenous Dogs, and the strokes or poysonsome stings of other creatures . . . ; to conclude, it is given against all poysons whatsoever, as also against many most grievous diseases."[63] Once again it is impossible to tell how much an accepted authority like Topsell had to do in perpetuating the old errors. Even when he brings the error up only to refute it, he is involuntarily prolonging its life.[64]

Thomas Fuller too put faith in the unicorn because of its

---

[58] *Ibid.,* p. 554.

[59] *Works,* ed. Keynes, II, 273.

[60] *Op. cit.,* p. 554.

[61] *Works,* ed. Keynes, II, 273. Topsell also speaks of "*Aelianus,* who only ascribeth to the same this wonderful force against poyson and most grievous diseases." *Op. cit.,* p. 555. And Browne says that "Aelian extolleth, who was the first and only man of the Ancients who spake of the medical vertue of any Unicorn." *Works,* ed. Keynes, II, 275-276.

[62] Topsell, *op. cit.,* p. 556. Cf. Browne, *Works,* ed. Keynes, II, 276.

[63] *Op. cit.,* p. 558. Robert Lovell affords a good example of the general belief in the unicorn's horn being a cure-all: "They stop fluxes of the belly, *gonorrhaea's,* whites, the bleeding at the nose, and hemorrhoides." They help even heart trouble! *A Compleat History of Animals and Minerals,* 2 vols. in one (Oxford, 1661), II, 96.

[64] The very fact that he devotes so many pages to testing the belief in the efficacy of the unicorn's horn proves the crying need for such testing. Such books as Peter Lum's *Fabulous Beasts* (London, n.d.) and P. Ansell Robin's *Animal Lore in English Literature* (London, 1932) prove the persistence of these legends. Lum notes (p. 58) that science continued to believe in the unicorn until Cuvier's time (early nineteenth century).

mention in the Bible.[65] The travelers themselves played their supporting role.[66] And Du Bartas' description of the animal right along with beavers and swans and roosters certainly had its effect upon popular belief.[67] A book like John Guillim's *A Display of Heraldrie*, read to be sure for other purposes, but very widely read, made its own impression with such dogmatic statements as "his *Horne* is supposed to be the most powerfull *Antidote* against *poison*."[68] And finally a picture-loving century found representations of the unicorn not only in Guillim but in Aldrovandi[69] and Samuel Bochart.[70]

Aside from his general interest in Egypt and hieroglyphics, Browne appears to have been especially fascinated by the Nile. His chapter on the subject[71] is very detailed. Two of the aspects he studied were the scarcity of rain in the Nile valley and the regular overflow of the river. Of the first he wrote: "It is affirmed by many, and received by most, that it never raineth in Egypt, the river supplying that defect, . . . but this must also be received in a qualified sense."[72] This was a matter of such

---

[65] *The History of the Worthies of England*, ed. John Nichols, 2 vols. (London, 1811), II, 54.

[66] Cf. Richard Hakluyt, *The Principal Navigations...of the English Nation*, 12 vols. (Glasgow, 1903-05), VIII, 157 *et passim*.

[67] *The Works of Du Bartas*, ed. Holmes, Lyons, and Linker, 3 vols. (Chapel Hill, 1935-40), II, 387.

[68] Fourth ed., London, 1660, p. 175.

[69] *De quadrupedibus solidipedibus* (Bologna, 1639), p. 415.

[70] *Hierozoicon* (Frankfurt, 1675), Pt. I, pp. 955-956. Another well-recognized antipathy was that between spider and toad. Here too Browne conducted his own experiment: "...having in a Glass included a Toad with several Spiders, we beheld the Spiders without resistance to sit upon his head and pass over all his body..." *Works*, ed. Keynes, II, 296. He says further that "solemn stories have been written of their combats." *Ibid.* Undoubtedly what he has in mind is the sort of story Topsell tells. The latter heard one "from the mouth of a true honourable man,...the good Earl of Bedford," who saw a fight in which the toad finally "swelled and broke in pieces." *The History of Serpents*, in Topsell, *op. cit.*, p. 729. A second story Topsell took from Erasmus. In this, a toad, having perched on the mouth of a sleeping monk, friends carried the monk to a spider's web: "And assoon as the Spyder saw her adversary the Toad, she...descended down upon the Toad." The poisoned amphibian then leapt off the monk's mouth and "swelled to death." And Topsell concludes: "And thus much may suffice for the antipathy of nature betwixt the Toad and the Spyder." *Ibid.*

[71] *Works*, ed. Keynes, III, 216-227.

[72] *Works*, ed. Keynes, III, 225.

moment that the Royal Society sent with a gentleman bound for Egypt the query "whether it rain there at any time."[73] Bacon emphasized the same feature.[74] Browne took exception also to another opinion that "confineth its [the Nile's] Inundation, and positively affirmeth, it constantly encreaseth the seventeenth day of June."[75] And he went on to speak of the river's earth "by the weight whereof (as good Authors report) they have unto this day a knowledge of its increase."[76] One of the "good Authors" was Lord Bacon, who maintained that the earth of the Nile would not change weight until June 17th.[77] Another query put to the Royal Society's man was "whether the earth of Egypt, adjoyning to the river, preserved and weighed daily, keeps the same weight till the 17th of June; and then grows daily heavier, with the increase of the river."[78] Later the Society decided to make its own experiments:

Upon inquiring what alteration had happened to the *terra Nilotica*, which had been ordered to be weighed and exposed to the air? Mr. Aston answered, that upon the 7th of May there were weighed out, and put into an exact pair of fine scales, three drachms, thirty-seven grains, and 17/20 of that earth, being all the parcel given by Dr. Plot; but that the poise since that time was not sensibly altered.[79]

Often the very age of an error helped to prolong a belief in it. This was eminently true of such notions as the elephant's sup-

---

[73] Birch, *The History of the Royal Society*, I, 297. Entry for August 26, 1663.
[74] *The Works of Francis Bacon*, ed. Spedding, etc., II, 587.
[75] *Works*, ed. Keynes, III, 223.
[76] *Works*, ed. Keynes, III, 224.
[77] *Works*, ed. Spedding, etc., II, 579. While we are arraigning Browne for credulity, we should not forget that an authority like Bacon, as the *DNB* reminds us in its article on that author, accepted such things as the belief that "the blood-stone is good for them that bleed at the nose," the "report" of "the writers of natural magic" that "the heart of an ape worn near the heart, comforteth the heart and increaseth audacity," and the notion that water is congealed into crystals.
[78] Birch, *The History of the Royal Society*, I, 299.
[79] *Ibid.*, IV, 204. Entry for May 16, 1683. But there the matter was not allowed to rest; later was "communicated an observation of the weight of the earth of the Nile about the time of the overflowing of that river, but especially a relenting of a piece of nitroon or nitre, brought from Aegypt, which continually wet the papers, on which it lay, both in rains and dry weather, from the middle of June till about the end of September." *Ibid.*, p. 220. Entry for October 24, 1683.

posed inability to bend his knees because he had no joints[80] and the supposed blindness of the mole. The latter misconception stems in part from Aristotle, who states:

All viviparous animals except moles have eyes. A person might, however, conclude from the following observation, that it has eyes, though it is quite without them, for it certainly does not see at all, nor has it any external eyes; but, when the skin is taken off, there is a place for the eyes, and the iris of the eye is in the place which it would naturally occupy on the outside, as if they had been wounded in their birth, and the skin had grown over the place.[81]

Batman had a way of stating such beliefs categorically so that later generations were inclined to accept his judgment: ". . . he [the mole] is dampned in everlastynge blyndenesse and derknesse, and is withoute eyen."[82] Those mild apostates from prosaic truth, the poets, were also to blame, Shakespeare, and Du Bartas, and Ford. But most to blame of all was the proverb. Topsell's "These Beasts are all blinde and want eyes, and therefore came the proverb *Talpa caecior, Tuphloteros aspalacos*, blinder then a Mole,"[83] might have been partially corrected by what he later said. But the human mind seems to be appealed to by what is explicit, not to say categorical. This was still another factor to make Browne feel he was rolling the stone of Sisyphus up a steep hill. In contending against such odds, he was occasionally inclined to be explicit himself: "That Moles are blind and have no eyes, though a common opinion, is received with much variety; . . . for that they have eyes in their head is manifest unto any, that wants them not in his own . . ."[84]

The belief that the lion is afraid of the cock had Pliny's authority, which, one might assume, would be enough to bury it:

---

[80] In a footnote in the 1835-36 Wilkin edition, Edward W. Brayley says that, even in his time, it was the custom for elephant trainers to demonstrate that the elephant could kneel; " . . . but I never saw this done, (and I have been present many times on such occasions,) without observing that it was witnessed with astonishment and almost with incredulity, by several persons present, whether the exhibition has been in London or in a provincial town." *Works*, ed. Wilkin, II, 390-391.

[81] *Aristotle's History of Animals*, trans. Richard Cresswell (London, 1862), p. 13. Aristotle was right about the species known in Greece.

[82] *Batman uppon Bartholome* (London, 1582), Bk. XVIII, chap. 102.

[83] *The History of Four-footed Beasts*, in Topsell, *op. cit.*, p. 389.

[84] *Works*, ed. Keynes, II, 250-251.

"Marching thus proudly as they [cocks] doe, the very Lions (which of all wild beasts be most courageous) stand in feare and awe of them, and will not abide the sight of them."[85] Batman did not for a moment question Pliny's word: "The Lion dreadeth and abhorreth [the Cock]."[86] And neither did Thomas Lupton.[87] Topsell ran true to form with his "a Lyon is afrayd of a cock,"[88] while Du Bartas brought his own confirmation when he referred to the cock as "the Lyons terror."[89] We think of Reginald Scot, the author of *The Discoverie of Witchcraft*, as being for his time an unusually enlightened person; yet Scot wrote: "A man would hardly beleeve, that a cocks combe or his crowing should abash a puissant lion; but that the experience hereof hath satisfied the whole world."[90] But more extraordinary than these was James I's own personal experiment, vouched for by George Hakewill in his *Apologie*, in which the monarch is represented as being surprised to discover that the king of beasts was not frightened by a rooster's crowing.[91] More significant still is the title of a pamphlet found in *The Harleian Miscellany*: "A Question of the Cock, and Whether His Crowing Affrights the Lion? Being one of those Questions handled in the weekly conferences of Monsieur Renaudot's Bureau d'Adresses, at Paris."[92] This entertaining pamphlet was translated into English in 1640. The first interlocutor, completely credulous, traces the belief back to Phidias.[93] He reasons that both animals are solar, but the cock more so than the lion, "whence it comes to pass, that the Cock hath a pre-eminence over the Lion."[94] The second speaker is the skeptic. He says the belief must be reckoned "among divers other vulgar ones." But the third, playing a Socratic role, holds that we must not dismiss the authority of the Ancients so lightly;

---

85 *Naturall Historie or The Historie of the World*, trans. Philemon Holland, 2 vols. in one (London, 1601), I, 279.
86 *Batman uppon Bartholome* (London, 1582), p. 183 verso.
87 *A Thousand Notable Things of Sundrie Sorts* (London, 1595), p. 43.
88 *The Historie of Foure-footed Beastes* (London, 1607), p. 123.
89 *His Divine Weekes and Workes* (London, 1641), p. 46.
90 London, 1654, p. 70.
91 Oxford, 1630, p. 13.
92 *The Harleian Miscellany*, 12 vols. (London, 1808-11), IV, 298-301.
93 *Ibid.*, p. 298.
94 *Ibid.*, p. 299.

the theory is not at all unreasonable.[95] And so Browne, thinking perhaps of the royal experiment, but actually giving an example from the Prince of Bavaria, concludes: "Whether a Lion be also afraid of a Cock, as is related by many, and believed by most, were very easie in some places to make trial."[96]

Still another misconception that can be traced straight back to the Classics is that of the swan song. Here again Aristotle was in part responsible, though that archliar Pliny—mirabile dictu!— denies the whole thing.[97] The Stagirite founded the belief on experience: "Swans have the power of song, especially when near the end of their life, for they then fly out to sea, and some persons, sailing near the coast of Libya, have met many of them in the sea singing a mournful song, and have afterwards seen some of them die."[98] Two well-known ornithologists were apparently willing to accept the belief. Aldrovandi went on record as follows:

Ea enim cum duplici reflexione, tubae bellicae figuram exactissime repraesentet, qua quamlibet tam acutorum, quam gravium sonorum[?] varietatem modulantes tubicines effingere solent, natura nihil frustra facere, neque etiam actionem ullam sine idoneis, functionique accommodatis instrumentis obire soleat, minime vulgari organi argumento facile inducor, ut verisimiliorem eorum esse credam sententiam, qui dulce melos, praesertim morti vicinos cantare dicunt.[99]

And Pierre Belon has a significantly French way of making Aristotle say "que les Cygnes chantent quand ils veulent mourir," mais "il ne le dit pas pour les avoir ouys."[100] An even more famous ornithologist, Francis Willughby, fellow of the Royal Society, is still willing to grant the legend some credence: "The Wind-pipe reflected in form of a Trumpet seems to be so contrived and formed by nature for modulating the voice. Hence

---

[95] *Ibid.*, p. 300.
[96] *Works*, ed. Keynes, II, 296.
[97] *Naturall Historie*, trans. Philemon Holland, 2 vols. in one (London, 1601), I, 282: "Some say that the Swans sing lamentably a little before their death, but untruly, I suppose: for experience in many hath shewed the contrarie."
[98] *Aristotle's History of Animals*, trans. Richard Cresswell (London, 1862), p. 244.
[99] *Ulyssis Aldrovandi, Ornithologiae tomus tertius ac postremus*, 3 vols. in one (Bologna, 1645), III, 20.
[100] *L'Histoire de la Nature des Oyseaux* (Paris, 1555), p. 151.

what the Ancients have delivered concerning the singing of
Swans (if it be true, which I much doubt) seems chiefly to this
bird [the wild swan], and not to the tame Swan."[101] Opposite
this passage in the Bodleian copy an early emender has written
in pen a part of Browne's own account in refutation. And finally
a scientific observer, Charles Waterton, who lived less than a
hundred years ago, took good care to watch a swan dying to
test the theory. The swan, he found, made no sound at all. James
E. Harting, who tells the story, utters "a warning to ornithologists not to indulge in the extravagances of romance—a propen-
sity not altogether unknown in these our latter times."[102] Perhaps Browne will not be accused of stabbing a corpse when he
writes: ". . . from great Antiquity . . . the Musical note of Swans
hath been commended, and that they sing most sweetly before
their death. . . . Surely he that is bit with a Tarantula, shall never
be cured by this Musick; and with the same hopes we expect to
hear the harmony of the Spheres."[103]

In discussing the pelican, Sir Thomas was dealing with a
double, not to say triple, difficulty, though here he did not have
to counter the Classics. The pelican was a favorite subject for
pictorial treatment, and it will be recalled that Browne introduced the bird in the section "Of many things questionable as
they are commonly described in Pictures."[104] The ability of art
to print an indelible impression on people's minds is remarkable. Aldrovandi, for example, carries an elaborate full-page
illustration of the pelican plunging its bill into its breast and of
the blood spurting into the mouths of its young ones who crouch
below.[105] As noted above, the legend is not classical in origin;

---

[101] *Ornithology* (London, 1678), p. 357. Since this is the edition to which
John Ray made considerable additions, the statement presumably had Ray's
blessing. This kind of rationalizing continued long past Browne's time.
Cf. T. D. Fosbroke's *Encyclopedia of Antiquities*, 2 vols. (London, 1840),
II, 1031: "The wild swan of the North has a note, or song, and the Ancients
only erred in applying it to all swans." And Fosbroke cites recent authority.
[102] *The Ornithology of Shakespeare* (London, 1871), p. 203.
[103] *Works*, ed. Keynes, II, 290-292.
[104] *Works*, ed. Keynes, III, 89-91.
[105] *Ornithologiae tomus tertius ac postremus*, 3 vols. in one (Bologna,
1645), III, 47. Pierre Belon adds his confirmation: "Quand le Serpent a
tué les petits du Pelican, qui fait son nid contre terre, les peres en pleurent,
et se batants la poictrine se sont sortir du sang, dont les petits retournent

one theory is that it derives from Egyptian monuments, though there the bird appears more like a flamingo. Batman gives the story to us substantially as it was believed in Browne's century: ". . . the mother smyteth her selfe in her syde, that the bloudde renneth out, and shedeth that hotte bloudde upon the bodyes of her chyldren. And by vertu of the bloude the byrdes that were before deed quycken ayen."[106] Significantly, the authority here given is a gloss to the Bible, for the Fathers early perceived how useful the legend might be in supporting the Eucharist. It was useful too in heraldry, and John Guillim reproduces on a shield a vivid sketch in miniature, with the description: "He beareth, Gules, a *Pellican* in her nest, with wings displayed, feeding of her *young ones.*"[107] This was the feature invariably stressed, a feature that Du Bartas probably did as much as anyone to fix:

> The other, kindly, for her tender Brood
> Tears her own bowells, trilleth-out her blood
> To heal her young, and in a wondrous sort
> Unto her Children doth her life transport:
> For finding them by some fell Serpent slain,
> She rents her breast and doth upon them rain
> Her vitall humour; whence recovering heat,
> They by her death, another life do get.[108]

The story was of course ultimately rationalized; in William Houghton's words, when the pelican is feeding its young from the fishy contents of its pouch, the red tip of the lower mandible is pressed against its breast, "and this has been supposed to lie at the bottom of the fable that the bird feeds its young ones with its own blood."[109] The marginal commentator who supplemented Willughby's *Ornithology*, doubtless an eighteenth-century au-

---

à vie." *L'Histoire de la Nature des Oyseaux* (Paris, 1555), p. 154. Cf. also Konrad von Gesner, *De historia animalium* (Basel, 1599), p. 842.

[106] *Batman uppon Bartholome* (London, 1582), Bk. XII, chap. 29.

[107] *A Display of Heraldrie* (4th ed.; London, 1660), p. 225.

[108] *His Divine Weekes and Workes* (London, 1641), p. 46. Shakespeare used the figure several times. That there was some confusion in his mind about the usual associations is to be seen in the passage from *Richard II*, II, i, 124 ff.

[109] *Gleanings from the Natural History of the Ancients* (London, [1879]), p. 190. Houghton says the story applies better to the vulture than the pelican.

thority, properly classified the legend as a "Vulgar Error."[110] But he might have saved himself his pains because poetry as well as the church had found in the image a most valuable ally. And they were not willing to let it go.

Whereas the pelican was taken as a symbol of paternal or maternal affection, the viper was often seen as representing filial ingratitude; so that Shakespeare would more appropriately have called Goneril and Regan "viperous" than "pelican" daughters. "That the young Vipers," Browne wrote, "force their way through the bowels of their Dam, or that the female Viper in the act of generation bites off the head of the male, in revenge whereof the young ones eat through the womb and belly of the female, is a very ancient tradition."[111] And he concluded that "the Tradition be untrue."[112] Pliny might be expected to support the belief,[113] but Aristotle would not: "The little vipers are produced in a membrane, which they rupture on the third day, and sometimes they make their escape by eating their way through the mother."[114] Again, what happened was that the Fathers found this legend useful, and Jerome and Basil lent it the sanction of their great names. The approach was normally through the "generation of vipers" passage; and there was some stretching of the Biblical text to make it cover the classical example. This is what Thomas Lupton had in mind when he wrote: "The young Vipers that springes of the same [mother], doo eate or gnawe a sunder their mothers Bellye, thereby comming or bursting foorth. . . . You may see, they were a towardly kind of people, that Christ called the generation of Vipers."[115] But once more it was Batman who doubtless set the tone with his version: "For when hir wombe draweth to the time of whelping, the whelpes abideth not covenable time nor kinde passing, but gnaweth and fretteth the sides of their dam, and they come so

[110] Francis Willughby's *Ornithology* (London, 1678), p. 328.
[111] *Works*, ed. Keynes, II, 237.
[112] *Works*, ed. Keynes, II, 239.
[113] *Naturall Historie*, trans. Philemon Holland, 2 vols. in one (London, 1601), I, 302.
[114] *Aristotle's History of Animals*, trans. Richard Cresswell (London, 1862), p. 137.
[115] *A Thousand Notable Things of Sundrie Sorts* (London, 1595), p. 120.

into this world . . . with the death of the breeder."[116] And the Royal Society continued its experiments on the subject into the 1660's: "Mr. Boyle related, that the viper-catchers find in the bag, wherein they keep their vipers, young ones among the old, and the old ones whole and sound."[117] Topsell's chapter on the subject is built much like Browne's. He gives the authorities on both sides. He quotes Pliny and cites several of the Fathers in confirmation, but goes on to tell the experience of modern authors who themselves had made the experiment only to find "that they [vipers] engendered, brought forth, and conceived like other Creatures, without death or ruine of Male and Female."[118] But here again such refutation made no impression on the poets, who found in the theory a lasting symbol of ingratitude:

> Thou mak'st th' ingratefull Viper (at his birth)
> His dying Mothers belly to gnaw forth.[119]

Du Bartas may also have been responsible in part for continuing the story of the glowworm's light:

> New-Spain's Cucuio, in his forhead brings
> Two burning Lamps, two underneath his wings;
> Whose shining Rayes serve oft, in darkest night,

---

116 *Batman uppon Bartholome* (London, 1582), p. 386. Cf. also: "The female byteth of . . . the head of the male." *Ibid.*, Bk. XVIII, chap. 117. Cf. also Alexander Ross: "The Vipers generation by the death of the mother proved, and objections to the contrary refuted." *Arcana microcosmi* (London, 1652), p. 144.

117 Birch, *The History of the Royal Society*, I, 349. Entry for December 21, 1663. Cf. also an entry for July 17, 1661, which records that Mr. Croune "was desired to keep the slow-worm, in order to see, whether the young one would eat through its belly." *Ibid.*, p. 34.

118 *The History of Serpents*, in Topsell, *op. cit.*, p. 802. Samuel Bochart similarly rejected the theory, saying that, though many Ancients believed it, Theophrastus and Aelian opposed it. See *Hierozoicon* (Frankfurt, 1675), Pt. II, p. 364.

119 Du Bartas, *His Divine Weekes and Workes* (London, 1641), p. 51. See also the important notes in *The Works of Du Bartas*, ed. Holmes, Lyons, and Linker, 3 vols. (Chapel Hill, 1935-40), II, 383, 385. See especially the notes for the fifth and sixth days of the "First Week." Cf. Dryden's *Absalom*, ll. 1012-15:

> "Against themselves their witnesses will swear,
> Till viper-like their mother Plot they tear;
> And suck for nutriment that bloody gore,
> Which was their principle of life before."

Th' imbroider's hand in royall Works to light:
Th' ingenious Turner, with a wakefull eye,
To polish fair his purest Ivory:
The Usurer to count his glistring treasures:
The learned Scribe to limn his golden measures.[120]

Browne was obviously interested in the problem, to the extent of experimentation: "Wondrous things are promised from the Glow-worm; from thence perpetual lights are pretended, and waters said to be distilled which afford a lustre in the night; . . . But hereto we cannot with reason assent."[121] The whole controversy turned on whether the light could be preserved after the glowworm's death. America, as Du Bartas implied, played its part, the Indians, according to Oviedo, having got the phosphorescent paste with which they smeared their faces from *cucuyos* or fireflies.[122] Bacon was willing to make some concession: "Glow-worms have their shining while they live, or a little after."[123] But certain other authorities had no such reservations; Thomas Lupton, for instance, was quite explicit in maintaining that the light may be preserved after the insect's death, and that the luminous material "will give such a light in the dark, as the moon doth, when she shines in a bright night."[124] Throughout *Pseudodoxia* Browne was doing his best not to be dogmatic; but there were limits, and here he braces: ". . . how to make perpetual lights, and sublunary moons thereof as is pretended, we rationally doubt, though not so sharply deny, with Scaliger and Muffetus."[125]

The whole phenomenon was one with which the Royal Society concerned itself: "Dr. Slare said, that he had kept a glow-worm six days after it was dead, during which time the shining was discernible, but gradually decreased: and that the

---

[120] *His Divine Weekes and Workes* (London, 1641), p. 45.
[121] *Works*, ed. Keynes, II, 299. E. S. Merton often associates such natural phenomena with Browne's concept of the nature of light in general. See *Science and Imagination in Sir Thomas Browne* (New York, 1949), p. 145, n. 2.
[122] *His Divine Weekes and Workes* (London, 1641), p. 45.
[123] *The Works of Francis Bacon*, ed. Spedding, etc., II, 456 (in *Sylva Sylvarum*).
[124] *A Thousand Notable Things of Sundrie Sorts* (London, 1595), Bk. IV, chap. 40; Bk. VIII, chap. 84.
[125] *Works*, ed. Keynes, II, 301.

liquor separated from the body shined four or five hours."[126] Thomas Pope Blount questioned the light's continuance but, in the course of his argument, cited powerful authorities on the other side: "Thereof Perpetual Lights are pretended, and Waters said to be distill'd, which afford a Lustre in the Night; and this is asserted by Cardan, Albertus, Gaudentinus [*sic*], Mizaldus, and many more."[127] When Blount gave his refutation, it is significant that the authority he relied on especially was Sir Thomas himself.[128] But the closest account of all to Browne's was that of Thomas Moffett. "Whether or no," wrote the latter, "the Glowworm being dead doth retain its splendor and shining, is wont to be a question," and went on to say that "experience teacheth the contrary" and that he himself had put it to the test. Moreover, he assailed the theory's proponents in claiming to make perpetual light "as if they would bring down the Moon from heaven."[129] In an identical context Browne said that they pretended "to make . . . sublunary moons thereof."[130] The mistake that Moffett made, along with so many of his contemporaries, was to state his

---

[126] Birch, *The History of the Royal Society*, IV, 356. Entry for January 14, 1684/5. Cf. also *ibid.*, p. 297 (bis). Entries for May 14, 1684. The general interest may be seen in an entry for May 25, 1664 (*ibid.*, I, 431), which records of a moorish place near Kellington that horses' hoofs and men's feet left an imprint on the grass "much more fiery than glow-worms."

[127] *A Natural History* . . . (London, 1693), p. 311.

[128] *Ibid.*, p. 313.

[129] *The Theater of Insects*, in Topsell, *op. cit.*, p. 979. As noted earlier, when the revised and enlarged edition of Topsell appeared in 1658, Moffett's book was chosen to be translated and subjoined as the authority on insects. The Latin version, which had appeared in 1634, is listed in *A Catalogue of the Libraries of the Learned Sir Thomas Brown, and Dr. Edward Brown, His Son* (London, 1711), p. 18, No. 51.

[130] *Works*, ed. Keynes, II, 301. Cf. also Moffett: "If a certain number of those that have no wings . . . be put into a clear Crystal glass . . . with a little grass, they may perchance give light for the space of some 12 daies, if every day fresh grasse be put to them; but at the length as they languish and faint away, so the light by little and little is remitted and slackned, and in the end they dying (as before is said) it is totally extinguished." *The Theater of Insects*, in Topsell, *op. cit.*, p. 979.
Cf. Browne: "As we have observed in some, which preserved in fresh grass have lived and shined eighteen days; but as they declined, and the luminous humor dryed, their light grew languid, and at last went out with their lives." *Works*, ed. Keynes, II, 300.
With Moffett's "afterwards they distil them through an Alembick, and keep the water in a clear glass" (p. 979), compare Browne's "waters said to be distilled which afford a lustre in the night" (*Works*, ed. Keynes, II, 299).

opponents' point of view as if he believed it: "Such a light doth this water or liquor give, by report, that in the darkest night any one may read and write."

It may well be that with the chameleon we have a case where Hamlet's famous words determined in part what people were to believe. Following his usual practice, Browne states his problem at the outset: "Concerning the Chameleon there generally passeth an opinion that it liveth only upon air . . . All which notwithstanding, upon enquiry I find the assertion mainly controvertible, and very much to fail in the three inducements of belief."[131] In 1635 Juan Eusebio Nieremberg had made the unqualified assertion: "Non alio quam aëris alimento chamaeleon vivit, iuxta Plinium et Solinum."[132] Browne would have said that the authority of Pliny was alone sufficient to call the theory into question. Bacon resorted to a piece of rationalization and therefore was probably not thought of as taking a definite side:

He feedeth not only upon air, (though that be his principal sustenance,) for sometimes he taketh flies, as was said; yet some that have kept chameleons a whole year together, could never perceive that ever they fed upon any thing else but air, and might observe their bellies to swell after they had exhausted the air.[133]

And the highly respected traveler, George Sandys, corroborates the theory, saying that "surely aire is their principal sustenance."[134] Even Topsell conceded that "it cannot be denied that it is *Oviparum patientissimum famis*: that is, The most induring famin among all other Egge-breeding-beasts, for it fasteth many times eight moneths: yea, a whole year together."[135] Du Bartas

---

[131] *Works*, ed. Keynes, II, 257-258.
[132] *Historia naturae* (Antwerp, 1635), p. 121.
[133] *The Works of Francis Bacon*, ed. Spedding, etc., II, 461.
[134] Samuel Purchas, *Purchas His Pilgrimes*, 5 vols. (London, 1625), II, 904.
[135] *The History of Serpents*, in Topsell, *op. cit.*, p. 672. Browne appears to have followed Topsell rather closely. Cf. Topsell: "I will also adde the description that *Scaliger* maketh thereof. For he saith, that when *Johannes Landius* was in the farthest parts of *Syria*, he saw five Chamaeleons, whereof he bought one, which with his tongue did very suddenly take off a Fly from his breast . . . : which thing seemed new and strange unto them which heretofore thought that a Chamaeleon lived only by the air" (*ibid.*, p. 673) with Browne: " . . . others have experimentally refuted it, as namely Johannes Landius, who in the relation of Scaliger, observed a Chameleon to lick up a fly from his breast . . . " (*Works*, ed. Keynes, II, 258).

had his own poetic version, in one of Sylvester's less happy lines: "And (food-less else) of th' Aire alonely lives."[136] The mollusclike nature of the story may be seen in T. M. Harris' *The Natural History of the Bible*: "It is a common tradition that the chameleon lives on air"[137] (note the unconscious use of the present tense). However, Harris tells of the experiment of the eighteenth-century traveler Fredrik Hasselquist, author of *Voyages and Travels in the Levant*,[138] who kept a chameleon for twenty-four days without food; but then "it waxed lean and suffered from hunger."[139]

Our ancestors were nothing if not extremists. Whereas the chameleon with them must have represented the limit of abstemiousness, the ostrich must have stood for gourmandizing at its worst (perhaps it is no accident that, in *Pseudodoxia*, the chapter on one follows the chapter on the other). The usual picture of the ostrich holding a horseshoe in its bill showed how people regularly thought of its eating habits. "The common opinion of the Ostrich . . . conceives that it digesteth Iron," says Browne, "and this is confirmed by the affirmations of many . . . Notwithstanding upon enquiry we find it very questionable, and the negative seems most reasonably entertained . . ."[140] The whole argument turned on whether the bird digested or merely swallowed iron! Pliny stood where he might be expected,[141] and he had some illustrious progeny. Batman, shall we say, swallows everything, including the sinker;[142] and Du Bartas refers to the ostrich, "whose greedy stomack steely gads digests."[143] During the Middle Ages a confirming element had come in with the Arabian proverb "stupid as an ostrich," which was based on that bird's tendency to swallow iron and

---

[136] *His Divine Weekes and Workes* (London, 1641), p. 50.

[137] London, 1824, pp. 76-77.

[138] London, 1766.

[139] T. M. Harris, *The Natural History of the Bible* (London, 1824), pp. 76-77.

[140] *Works*, ed. Keynes, II, 267-268.

[141] *Naturall Historie*, trans. Philemon Holland, 2 vols. in one (London, 1601), I, 270.

[142] *Batman uppon Bartholome* (London, 1582), p. 187 verso.

[143] *His Divine Weekes and Workes* (London, 1641), p. 46. See also Alexander Ross's *Arcana microcosmi* (London, 1652), p. 141: "I do not much wonder that the Ostridge can eat and digest iron."

stones.[144] And this theme was taken up by the travelers; Leo Africanus, for instance: "The ostrich is a silly and deafe creature, feeding upon any thing which it findeth, be it as hard and indigestable as yron."[145] Whereas Aldrovandi is inclined to question the belief,[146] so widely accepted an authority as Pierre Belon is on the side of the believers: "Et si nous considerions aussi bien la nature des petits oysillons, qui digerent les cailloux, et le sablon, nous ne trouverions si estrange que l'Autruche puisse digerer le fer."[147] But the other great authority, Francis Willughby, takes the middle ground: "It swallows Iron, Leather, Grass, Bread, Hair, and whatever else you offer it, promiscuously: Howbeit it doth not concoct Iron and other hard things, but avoids them entire by siege."[148] It is Willem Piso who has the art of expressing things most succinctly; so here: "Ferrum quoque et lapides deglutire amant, eaque inconcocta et integra per anum reddunt."[149] But the Royal Society was not satisfied; it went on experimenting. On March 28, 1672, a Mr. Burghill was commissioned to check in Africa on the question, "What the ostrich feeds upon."[150] The answer came back promptly: "They will swallow iron." A later entry records: "Dr. Brown [Sir Thomas' son] with some other physicians had dissected an ostrich: and had drawn up an account of his observations made in that dissection, which he now communicated to the Society."[151] It is possible to supplement this entry from the correspondence between Edward and his father. Sir Thomas paternally sent his son elaborate notes on the ostrich for use in his report to the Society.[152] But

[144] William Houghton, *Gleanings from the Natural History of the Ancients* (London, [1879]), pp. 196-197.
[145] Samuel Purchas, *Purchas His Pilgrimes*, 5 vols. (London, 1625), II, 849.
[146] *Ornithologiae*, 3 vols. (Frankfurt, 1610), I, 592. But once again Aldrovandi's account is full of such misleading statements as "Joannes Langius qui in horto Ducis Ferrariem Struthionem ferrum concoxisse sese observasse testatur." *Ibid.*
[147] *L'Histoire de la Nature des Oyseaux* (Paris, 1555), p. 233.
[148] *Ornithology* (London, 1678), p. 150.
[149] *De Indiae utriusque re naturali et medica libri quatuordecim* (Amsterdam, 1658), p. 84.
[150] Birch, *The History of the Royal Society*, III, 27.
[151] *Ibid.*, IV, 132.
[152] *Works*, ed. Keynes, V, 323-326.

Edward's own experiments came to naught; he fed his bird "a peece of iron which weighed two ounces and a half, which we found in the first stomack again not at all altered."[153] And Edward seemed mildly surprised that "ours died of a soden."[154]

With the tiger we have what is perhaps the best example of how etymology may operate to make a popular error last. Browne characteristically bases his refutation of the belief that the tiger is one of the swiftest animals on an eyewitness; he "cannot but observe, that Jacobus Bontius late Physitian at Java in the East Indies, as an ocular and frequent witness is not afraid to deny it; . . . indeed it is but a slow and tardigradous animal."[155] The confusion came through an identification with the river Tigris, an identification so complete that the creature was often spelled "Tigris." "Hath this name Tigris," wrote Batman, "for strong reese and swiftnesse, as that beast that is called Tigris, that runnethe with great swiftnesse."[156] There were many suggestions as to how this identification took place. Batman himself, for whom a single superlative is not enough, says that the "Tigris is the most swiftest beast in flight, as it were an arrow, for the Persians call an arrow Tigris."[157] Franzio offers another derivation: "Quod ad nomen attinet, lingua Armenica significat sagittam, unde etiam fluvius hoc nomine appellatus fuit, quod eius summa sit velocitas."[158] And it was to this theory

---

[153] *Works*, ed. Wilkin, I, 329. See page 129 *infra*, note 140.
[154] *Works*, ed. Wilkin, I, 329.
[155] *Works*, ed. Keynes, II, 306.
[156] *Batman uppon Bartholome* (London, 1582), p. 192.
[157] *Ibid.*, p. 382.
[158] Wolfgango Franzio, *Animalium historia sacra* (Amsterdam, 1653), p. 67. This book appears in *A Catalogue of the Libraries of the Learned Sir Thomas Brown, and Dr. Edward Brown, His Son* (London, 1711), p. 23, Item 28. Samuel Bochart has perhaps the most unusual explanation of all: "Et e natura eius est, ut faemina e vento concipiat. Proinde cursus eius est qualis venti, nec eam potest venatu quisquam assequi. Ecce alteram fabulam priore putidiorem, quaeque illam destruit"! *Hierozoicon* (Frankfurt, 1675), Pt. I, p. 795. The argument worked, of course, both ways. Thus, Juan Eusebio Nieremberg, discoursing of the river: "Graeca vero et Latina voce Tigris dicitur, quia instar tigridis bestiae nimia pernicitate decurrit. Tigris enim, ut habet Plinius, animal est tremendae velocitatis." *Historia naturae* (Antwerp, 1635), p. 497. Willem Piso also quotes this passage from Pliny, but only to refute it. *De Indiae utriusque re naturali et medica libri quatuordecim* (Amsterdam, 1658), p. 52. The travelers played their usual part. Purchas prints a passage from Fernández de Oviedo

that Topsell gave currency: "The word *Tigris* is an *Armenian* word, which signifieth both a swift Arrow, and a great River." And he went on to tell the old story of Bacchus being ferried over the river by a tiger: "Afterward *Bacchus* called that swift River by the name of that swift beast, Tiger."[159] And the etymologizing goes right on to the present day with the conjecture by the modern editors of Aristotle that "the root of 'tiger' is said to signify 'sharp,' 'swift,' or 'an arrow.' "[160] They refer then to Varro. Here then is a case where etymology so completely supported the old tradition that an epithet was adopted that, in its turn, continued that tradition. It is represented by Du Bartas' "light-foot Tigre."[161]

Browne, it has been observed, was just as much interested in the minute fauna as in the large; the spider was as fascinating to him as the elephant, perhaps more so. It is not surprising, therefore, to note his preoccupation with a little creature well known as the "deathwatch," a creature whose very name tended to perpetuate the superstitions connected with it. As Browne says: "Few ears have escaped the noise of the Dead-watch, that is, the little clickling sound heard often in many rooms, somewhat resembling that of a Watch; and this is conceived to be of an evil omen or prediction of some person's death: wherein notwithstanding there is nothing of rational presage or just cause of terrour unto melancholy and meticulous heads."[162] What brings the whole matter home, what makes us realize how immediate these superstitions were is Browne's last statement on the subject: "He that could extinguish the terrifying apprehensions hereof, might prevent the passions of the heart, and many cold sweats in Grandmothers and Nurses, who in the sickness of children, are so startled with these noises."[163] Sir

---

in which that gentleman cites the statement by Pliny. Samuel Purchas, *Purchas His Pilgrimes*, 5 vols. (London, 1625), III, 990.

[159] *The History of Four-footed Beasts*, in Topsell, *op. cit.*, pp. 547-548.

[160] *Works of Aristotle*, ed. J. A. Smith and W. D. Ross, 12 vols. (Oxford, 1908-52), IV, 501ª, note.

[161] *His Divine Weekes and Workes* (London, 1641), p. 51. Joannes Jonstonus, *An History of the Wonderful Things of Nature* (London, 1657), p. 236, concludes his chapter "Of Tatus and the Tyger" with this sentence: "It is a Creature so swift, that *Oppianus* compares it to the West wind."

[162] *Works*, ed. Keynes, II, 171-172.

[163] *Works*, ed. Keynes, II, 172.

Thomas made his own experiments and had often observed the insects "knock with a little proboscis or trunk against the side of the box" in which he was keeping them.[164] To him there was nothing more mysterious in the process than there was in the operation of a woodpecker on a somewhat smaller scale! But the Royal Society was not dissuaded by Browne's findings from making its own experiments: "Dr. Ent was desired to bring in at the next meeting his box of little animals, which make a noise, called the death-watch."[165] In the following century Dean Swift dismissed the legend in characteristic vein:

> But a Kettle of scalding hot Water injected,
> Infallibly cures the Timber affected:
> The Omen is broken, the Danger is over,
> The Maggot will die and the Sick will recover.

Another small animal in which Browne was interested was the ant:

> The wisdom of the Pismire is magnified by all, and in the Panegyricks of their providence we alwaies meet with this, that to prevent the growth of Corn which they store up, they bite off the end thereof . . . From whence ariseth a conceit that Corn will not grow if the extreams be cut or broken. But herein we find no security to prevent its germination; as having made trial in grains, whose ends cut off have notwithstanding suddenly sprouted, . . .[166]

Here again Sir Thomas has in mind the great authority Moffett, who headed his chapter, "The commendation of Pismires," and went into some details about their habits: "They creeping up to the top of the stalk, bite off the ears of Corn, and the young ones stay and gather them up, and the Chaffe being fallen off, they pull the Corn out of the husks, and then they carry it home; and the end of it being eaten off, if there be necessity, they set it at their doors a sunning."[167] Robert Lovell, writing fifteen years after Browne, was equally explicit; he speaks of pismires that "*get corne*, which they dry, and *bite* at both ends, that it grow not."[168] Bacon himself asked, "Who taught the ant to

---

164 *Ibid.*
165 Birch, *The History of the Royal Society*, I, 84. Entry for May 28, 1662.
166 *Works*, ed. Keynes, II, 301-302.
167 *The Theater of Insects*, in Topsell, *op. cit.*, p. 1075.
168 A *Compleat History of Animals and Minerals*, 2 vols. in one (Oxford, 1661), I, 281. John Robinson, *Endoxa* (London, 1658), pp. 133-134, wrote

bite the grains of corn that she lays up in her hill, lest they should sprout and so disappoint her hope?"[169] The belief goes back to the Ancients and was actively continued during the Middle Ages, Pliny, Aelian, Ovid, Virgil, Lucian, Zoroaster, Origen, Basil, and Epiphanius "all concurring in the opinion that ants cut off the heads of grain, to prevent their germinating."[170] Many centuries later the French Academy published a confirming letter, which was reprinted by Addison in a number of the *Guardian* "as a narrative of undoubted credit and authority."[171]

"The tradition is no less ancient," wrote Bacon, "that the wolf, if he see a man first, by aspect striketh a man hoarse."[172] And, if the tradition is strictly followed, by "hoarse" Bacon meant "dumb." Browne took up where Bacon left off: "Such a Story as the Basilisk is that of the Wolf concerning priority of vision, that a man becomes hoarse or dumb, if a Wolf have the advantage first to eye him."[173] The tale is one of the many that go back to Pliny, or at least for which Pliny was largely responsible.[174] Topsell cites the Pliny passage, but adds his own kind of rationalization: "But the meaning of this is, as we find in other writers, that if a Wolfe first see a man, the man is silent, and cannot speake, but if the man see the Wolfe, the Wolfe is silent and cannot cry, otherwise the tale is fabulous and superstitious."[175] Sir Thomas had the misfortune of being

---

as follows: "In the *center of the kernell of grain*, as the safest abditory, is the *scourse of germination*; which may and doth *escape the amputation of the extremes, by a knife*; but *not the terebration of the pis-mire*; though very small: The latter hindereth it from *sprouting*; so doth not the former."

[169] *The Works of Francis Bacon*, ed. Spedding, etc., I, 619. Translation at IV, 410.

[170] T. M. Harris, *The Natural History of the Bible* (London, 1824), pp. 11-12.

[171] No. 156. Part of the letter is as follows: "The corn which is laid up by ants would shoot under ground, if these insects did not take care to prevent it. They, therefore, bite off all the germs before they lay it up; ... Any one may make the experiment, and even see that there is no germ in their corn."

[172] *The Works of Francis Bacon*, ed. Spedding, etc., II, 648.

[173] *Works*, ed. Keynes, II, 205.

[174] *Naturall Historie*, trans. Philemon Holland, 2 vols. in one (London, 1601), I, 207.

[175] *The History of Four-footed Beasts*, in Topsell, *op. cit.*, p. 740.

held to account by the Southampton schoolmaster, Alexander Ross. The latter says of the wolf belief that Browne "did unadvisedly reckon this among his vulgar errors." Ross is inclined to justify one myth by analogy with another: "And what wonder is it, that the sight of a Wolf should make a man speechlesse, when the shadow of the Hyena, will make a Dog dumb." And he concludes with the magnificent peroration that Browne would be struck dumb too "if he were suddenly surprised by a Wolf"![176]

Browne was always ready to investigate the humblest aspects of life; and this was especially true if he felt that he could do his fellowman good by disabusing his mind of some untruth that affected his physical well-being. This is not merely the Christian but the doctor in him. The countryside was full of old wives' tales, of home remedies that were no remedies. One can imagine that Browne was grateful that Dr. James Primrose, eight years before the publication of *Pseudodoxia*, had relieved him of the responsibility of exposing medical errors.[177] But occasionally Sir Thomas felt that he must have his say. In one instance, it was the lowly wart that received his attention. He asks the rhetorical question, "what natural effects can reasonably be expected . . . when for Warts we rub our hands before the Moon."[178] And yet almost twenty years later the august body of the Royal Society was not above investigating extraordinary cures for this very trouble: "He [Dr. Pell] added, that a certain person, who had abundance of warts upon his hands, by washing them in the May-dew of several garden herbs, as balm, sage, etc. was perfectly cured of them before the end of May."[179] With Lord Bacon it was a case of an actual personal experience:

---

[176] *Arcana microcosmi* (London, 1652), p. 106. Ross is the same man who, in his *Medicus medicatus* (London, 1645), assailed Browne's *Religio medici*. See page 5 and note 16 *supra*.

[177] *Popular Errours. Or the Errours of the People in Physick*, trans. Robert Wittie (London, 1651). The book appeared first in Latin in 1638.

[178] *Works*, ed. Keynes, III, 157. John Brand late in the eighteenth century repeats this superstition virtually word for word from Browne. See *Observations on Popular Antiquities* (Newcastle upon Tyne, 1777), p. 97.

[179] Birch, *The History of the Royal Society*, I, 418. Entry for April 27, 1664.

The English ambassador's lady, who was a woman far from superstition, told me one day, she would help me away with my warts: whereupon she got a piece of lard, with the skin on, and rubbed the warts all over with the fat side; and amongst the rest, that wart which I had had from my childhood: then she nailed the piece of lard, with the fat towards the sun, upon a post of her chamber window, which was to the south. The success was, that within five weeks' space all the warts went quite away: and that wart which I had so long endured, for company.[180]

The lard "with the skin on" may have had some curative effect, but it may be justly questioned that its exposure to the south took part in the cure, even if it was nailed in my lady's chamber.

A superstition that Browne mentions only in passing was the *"Sortes Homericae,* or *Virgilianae"*: "A practise there is among us to determine doubtful matters, by the opening of a book, and letting fall a staff; which notwithstanding are ancient fragments of Pagan divinations."[181] He then gives examples from classical times, and notes that the practice extended to the Bible.[182] Wilkin recounts a story in which Sir Thomas' king, Charles I, tried the experiment while on visit to Oxford during the Civil Wars. Lord Falkland, in an unfortunate moment, persuaded Charles to open a copy of Virgil, "which every body knows was an usual kind of augury some ages past." The book opened at Dido's curse upon Aeneas, which applied in a phenomenal way to Charles's own case. The King was deeply disturbed and Falkland, hoping to improve matters, made them worse by trying the game on himself and turning up a passage that fitted him even better.[183]

Not quite so old but even more persistent was the belief in the sun's dancing on Easter, familiar to us through Suckling's well-known line. "We shall not, I hope," said Browne, "disparage the Resurrection of our Redeemer, if we say the Sun doth not dance on Easter day," and he added that he could not "conceive therein any more than a Tropical expression."[184]

---

[180] *The Works of Francis Bacon,* ed. Spedding, etc., II, 670.

[181] *Works,* ed. Keynes, III, 154.

[182] *Works,* ed. Keynes, III, 155.

[183] Wilkin's edition of Browne's *Works,* III, 179, note. John Brand describes the custom in his *Observations on Popular Antiquities* (Newcastle upon Tyne, 1777), p. 93.

[184] *Works,* ed. Keynes, III, 148-149.

John Brand, who lived on into the nineteenth century, was still struggling to prove the belief a popular error:

It is [note the present tense] a common Custom among the Vulgar and uneducated Part of the World, to rise before the Sun on Easter-day, and walk into the Fields: The Reason of which is to see the Sun Dance; which they have been told, from an old Tradition, always dances as upon that Day.... If therefore this Tradition hath any Meaning, it must be a metaphorical one.[185]

Still more significantly Brand puts in a personal note:

I have heard of, when a Boy, and cannot positively say whether I have not *seen* tried, an ingenious Method of making an artificial *Sun* Dance on Easter Sunday;—a Vessel full of Water was set out in the open Air, in which the reflected Sun *seemed to dance* from the *tremulous Motion* of the Water.[186]

In this connection we can think only of what John Gerard once wrote: "Thus much in general we may observe, that strange effects are naturally taken for miracles by weaker heads, and artificially improved to that apprehension by wiser."[187]

Doubtless Browne was himself unconscious of the fact that, like the others, he was continuing errors by their mere mention, often quite incidentally. This happens perhaps most frequently in connection with errors derived from classical times. It is probable he assumed that few any longer believed in them. The whole context, for instance, in which he casts the old story of Aeschylus' death is playful, and the very mention of Aelian as the authority for it at once throws doubt on its validity. Browne speaks of "Aeschilus, whose bald-pate was mistaken for a rock, and so was brained by a Tortoise which an Aegle let fall upon it."[188] If Sir Thomas had wished to put the final quietus on the legend, he might have mentioned that Pliny also had his version.[189] The odd tale about Crassus' having laughed only once also goes back to Pliny. Again Browne uses the circumstance merely as a springboard and, by the time he

---

[185] *Observations on Popular Antiquities* (Newcastle upon Tyne, 1777), p. 241.
[186] *Ibid.*, p. 247.
[187] *The Herball* (London, 1633), II, 372.
[188] *Works*, ed. Keynes, III, 326.
[189] *Naturall Historie*, trans. Philemon Holland, 2 vols. in one (London, 1601), I, 271: "And it was the fortune of the Poët *Aeschylus* to die by such a meanes.... An Aegle let fall a Tortoise, which light upon his head, dasht out his braines, and laid him asleepe for ever."

has finished his argument, has almost forgotten that he has used it at all: "The Relation of Lucillius, and now become common, concerning Crassus the grand-father of Marcus the wealthy Roman, that he never laughed but once in all his life ... is something strange."[190] Pliny's account is similar, except that he affords the Roman another grandchild: "It is said, that *Crassus* (grandfather to that *Crassus* who was slaine in Parthia) was never knowne to laugh all his life time."[191]

Better known was the story about the manner of Cleopatra's death. This appears to have stirred up considerable controversy in ancient times, the authorities involved including Galen, Plutarch, Propertius, and Strabo. Browne states the chief problem: "We might question the place; for some apply them [asps] unto her breast, which notwithstanding will not consist with the History ... "[192] In declaring for the arm, Sir Thomas was following the most recent and dependable authority. Dr. James Primrose had contended that history supported the arm: "Zonaras relates that there appeared no signe of death upon her, save two blew spots on her arme."[193] And he went on to argue that a bite on the arm would be more fatal. Another point emphasized by Browne was the fact that the bites could hardly be detected; he refers to them as "two small and almost insensible pricks ... found upon her arm."[194] Topsell, in his rather elaborate description of the event, stresses the same feature: "When an Asp hath bitten, it is a very difficult thing to espy the place bitten or wounded, even with most excellent eyes, as was apparent upon *Cleopatra* aforesaid." And he says further: "The pricks of the Asps teeth, are in appearance not much greater then the prickings of a needle, without all swelling, and very little bloud issueth forth."[195]

---

[190] *Works*, ed. Keynes, III, 310-311. With Browne's " ... he never laughed but once in all his life, and that was at an Ass eating thistles" (*ibid.*, p. 310), cf. Dryden's "The Man who laugh'd but once, to see an Ass / Mumbling to make the cross-grained Thistles pass" ("The Medal," ll. 145-146).

[191] *Naturall Historie*, trans. Philemon Holland, 2 vols. in one (London, 1601), I, 166.

[192] *Works*, ed. Keynes, III, 118.

[193] *Popular Errours. Or the Errours of the People in Physick*, trans. Robert Wittie (London, 1651), p. 29. Originally published in 1638.

[194] *Works*, ed. Keynes, III, 118.

[195] *The History of Serpents*, in Topsell, *op. cit.*, p. 635.

Even the fantastic story of Hannibal's device to work his way through the Alps had found its sponsor in modern times. Relying on the authority of Livy and Plutarch, Thomas Lupton had written in all seriousness: "Anniball, made a passage for him and his Souldiers through the harde Rocks of the Alpes to passe into Italie. For by heating and burning the stones with fire, and sprinckling Vineger thereon, he made them so softe, that they might fall easily in peeces, and that they might be sooner broken a sunder."[196] And, unfortunately, Lupton's book was the kind much more apt to be read than any truly scientific pamphlet. Browne's reaction to such a story is thoroughly characteristic of him: "That Annibal eat or brake through the Alps with Vinegar, may be too grosly taken, ... it may seem incredible, not only in the greatness of the effect, but the quantity of the efficient; and such as behold them, may think an Ocean of Vinegar too little for that effect."[197]

Appropriately Browne follows the Hannibal story with one concerning Archimedes: "That Archimedes burnt the ships of Marcellus, with speculums of parabolical figures, at three furlongs, or as some will have it, at the distance of three miles, sounds hard unto reason, and artificial experience: and therefore justly questioned by Kircherus ... "[198] The extraordinary thing about this story is that Bacon appears to have put some credence in it: "If burning-glasses could be brought to a great strength (as they talk generally of burning-glasses that are able to burn a navy) the percussion of the air alone by such a burning-glass would make no noise."[199] And clearly the Royal Society, some thirty years after the publication of *Pseudodoxia*, regarded the matter as not being wholly academic:

Concerning the latter paper of Dr. Vossius, treating of the burning-glass of Archimedes, Mr. Hooke declared, that he could not say, whether it were made in the manner described by the Dr. or not: but added, that he was sure, that a speculum made of a parabolical figure would much surpass one of the same size, made up of several specular plains . . . : this did not

---

[196] *A Thousand Notable Things of Sundrie Sorts* (London, 1595), p. 17.
[197] *Works*, ed. Keynes, III, 324.
[198] *Works*, ed. Keynes, III, 325.
[199] *The Works of Francis Bacon*, ed. Spedding, etc., II, 393.

solve that great question about burning-glasses, viz. how to make one of a determinate bigness, that shall burn at any distance assigned.[200]

One more classical story that defied disproof was the one about Aristotle and the Euripus.[201] Browne's version runs as follows:

> That Aristotle drowned himself in *Euripus*, as despairing to resolve the cause of its reciprocation, or ebb and flow seven times a day, . . . is generally believed amongst us. . . . Now that in this Euripe or fret of Negropont, and upon the occasion mentioned, Aristotle drowned himself, as many affirm, and almost all believe, we have some room to doubt.[202]

There was, of course, much general interest in tides, in what Browne himself calls "the Flux and Reflux of the Sea." Bacon wrote *De fluxu et refluxu maris*.[203] The Royal Society showed a similar active interest. We read such entries as: "Mr. Powle gave an account of some observations concerning tides, which he promised to give in more largely in writing before he went out of town"; and, "Sir Paul Neile moved, that those, who were employed to observe high tides, might be desired to observe, whether they are constantly accompanied with high winds."[204] But the interest did not always remain on this general level. In 1666 the important traveler and historian of Turkey, Paul Rycaut, was commissioned by the Society to make certain investigations in Turkey.[205] It is quite clear what the nature of

---

[200] Birch, *The History of the Royal Society*, III, 193. Entry for March 4, 1674/5. Earlier in the century so distinguished a scientist as John Napier, in fear of a Spanish invasion, worked on inventing a mirror that would burn ships at a distance. *A Short History of Science* by W. T. Sedgwick and H. W. Tyler (New York, 1917), p. 242.

[201] The ancient name of the strait between Chalcis (Euboea, Greece) and the mainland.

[202] *Works*, ed. Keynes, III, 297. In the last edition of *Pseudodoxia* to be published in his lifetime, Browne added an experiment recorded in *Les voyages du sieur Du Loir* (Paris, 1654). The Frenchman tells of having given a boatman a crown to put him in a convenient place "where for a whole day I might observe the same [the tides of Euripus]." His conclusion was that "it ebbeth and floweth by six hours, even as it doth at Venice, but the course thereof is vehement" (*Works*, ed. Keynes, III, 300). See also pp. 126-127 *infra*.

[203] *The Works of Francis Bacon*, ed. Spedding, etc., III, 47 ff.

[204] Birch, *The History of the Royal Society*, II, 133. Entries for December 12, 1666.

[205] *Ibid.*, p. 132. Rycaut was elected a member of the Society towards the end of 1666.

one inquiry was, quite clear that it probably had some connection with the old story of Aristotle and the Euripus, for in a
letter from Smyrna dated November 23, 1667 Rycaut writes
as follows:

The water runs out of the Euxine sea into the Propontis with a wonderful
swiftness, which is the more admirable in regard of the depth of the Bosphorus, being in the channel fifty or fifty five fathom water, and along the
land in most places, ships may lie ashore with their heads, and yet have
twenty fathom water at their sterns. Here are no tides to be observed, nor
that the water either rises or falls above a foot or two at the most, nor could
I ever learn certainly, which were the Euripi; I conjecture, they may be
some rocks at the mouth of the Bosphorus, which have diversity of tides,
according to the winds.[206]

In the foregoing study it has been farthest from my mind to
contend that Browne did not, from time to time, occupy himself with trifling matters. He was, at times, as Coleridge says, a
hunter of oddities and strangenesses. My purpose has been
merely to show that, when everything is considered, the balance weighs heavily on his side. In the main he was concerned
with things that were of live interest, not merely to the common people but often to the most enlightened minds of his
day. Certainly the Royal Society had among its members scientists recognized as preeminent during the last forty years of
the seventeenth century. For the others, Browne rested his
authority on books that were generally accepted as offering
the most dependable information on the subject, such as the
books by Topsell and Moffett and Willughby.[207] Linnaeus
might have set him right on certain phases of horticulture. But
unluckily Linnaeus was not born until the next century. On
the part of the critics, there has been a tendency to arraign
Browne for not knowing what was not discovered until the
century that followed his, in fact even until the nineteenth and

---

[206] *Ibid.*, p. 268.
[207] While discussing Browne's treatment of the lodestone, J. S. Finch
writes: "In naming such writers as Gilbert, Descartes, and Digby, he was
not dallying with worn-out learning, but was citing the most recent and
best-informed writers." *Sir Thomas Browne: A Doctor's Life of Science
and Faith* (New York, 1950), p. 156.

twentieth centuries. For all his mysticism, Sir Thomas never claimed any powers of clairvoyance. If he dealt with what seem to us trifles, it was because his age often busied itself with "trifles"; conceivably, a part of his very purpose was to expose those trifles so that men would have more time to devote to matters of serious import. Bacon frequently investigated in the hope of improving man's physical status; this was often Browne's objective also, though Browne was perhaps even more concerned to help man look out upon his world with a saner eye.[208] Though as doctor he knew the importance of *in corpore sano*, he was yet more interested in *mens sana*. To help his fellowman achieve the latter, he assembled the best authorities on many subjects, and he gave in addition the benefit of his own clear intelligence and reasoning powers.

---

[208] E. S. Merton, "Sir Thomas Browne's Scientific Quest," *Journal of the History of Medicine*, III (1948), 214-228, draws a sharp distinction between their two objectives.

GEORGE YOST

*

Sir Thomas Browne
and Aristotle

*

T HIS STUDY is concerned principally with Sir Thomas
Browne as a scholar of Aristotle. It is hoped that, incidentally, it will also throw a more general light on
Browne's scholarly methods as he works at his desk
under the circumstances of the seventeenth century and a medical practice.

ARISTOTLE THROUGH THE SEVENTEENTH CENTURY

From his position in the seventeenth century, Browne witnessed the climax of long-fought battles between Aristotle and
his opponents. With the Renaissance had come other systems
and philosophers old and new to dispute the hegemony granted
Aristotle by the church. Sixteenth-century humanists had tended
to follow Plato rather than Aristotle.[1] At the same time the
study of such rhetoricians as Cicero and Quintilian had brought
an outcry against the vagueness of Aristotle's concepts.[2] Much
more, the Reformation had had an antipathy to Aristotle because of the Aristotelian dogma that St. Thomas Aquinas had
woven into Catholicism.[3] Also, the clashing of many doctrines

---

[1] F. R. Johnson, *Astronomical Thought in Renaissance England* (Balti-
more, 1937), p. 83.
[2] Wilhelm Windelband, *A History of Philosophy*, trans. J. H. Tufts (New
York, 1901), p. 360.
[3] Richard Foster Jones, *Ancients and Moderns; A Study of the Background
of the Battle of the Books*, Wash. Univ. Stud., New Ser., Lang. and Lit.,
No. 6 (St. Louis, 1936), p. 152.

in the sixteenth century had brought about a revival of the ancient skeptical philosophy,[4] and its universal condemnation of philosophizing had made no exception of Aristotle's thought. This current continued unabated throughout the seventeenth century in René Descartes, Pierre Gassendi, Joseph Glanvill, and John Dryden.[5] Browne's *Religio medici*, therefore, found enthusiastic reception among mutually antagonistic religious sects because its underlying skepticism subordinated reason and smoothed out doctrinal differences.

Meanwhile, scientific minds were making discoveries, especially in astronomy, that undermined the authority of Aristotle.[6] Copernicus had dethroned the earth from its Ptolemaic position at the center of the universe and, so, had begun the process that eventually destroyed Aristotle's physics and astronomy, although the new astronomy was long in being accepted.[7] Kepler, using the data of Tycho Brahe, discovered the three laws of planetary motion that substituted mathematical relationships for Aristotle's cosmology.[8] With the newly discovered and improved telescope, Galileo found an unknown luminary among the "fixed stars," in a zone that Aristotle had said was changeless. He also discovered the satellites of Jupiter and the phases of Venus that illustrated the validity of the Copernican doctrine.[9]

Other sciences prospered at the expense of Aristotle's teach-

---

[4] L. I. Bredvold, *The Intellectual Milieu of John Dryden; Studies in Some Aspects of Seventeenth Century Thought* (Ann Arbor, 1934), pp. 16-27.
[5] *Ibid.*, pp. 62-72.
[6] Douglas McKie, "The Origins and Foundations of the Royal Society of London," in *The Royal Society, Its Origins and Founders*, ed. Sir Harold Hartley, F.R.S. (London, 1960), p. 3, has the reaction against tradition beginning not in the sciences but in the arts with their "close and accurate observation and delineation of plants and animals."
[7] W. C. D. Dampier-Whetham, *A History of Science and Its Relations with Philosophy and Religion* (Cambridge, 1931), pp. 119-124; A. R. Hall, *The Scientific Revolution, 1500-1800* (New York, 1954), p. 106; McKie, *op. cit.*, p. 2.
[8] Charles Singer, *A Short History of Science to the Nineteenth Century* (Oxford, 1941), pp. 204-205.
[9] *Ibid.*, pp. 206-208. William Gilbert, whose *De magnete* (London, 1600) established the science of terrestrial magnetism as an experimental study, aided the acceptance of the Copernican doctrine in England. Jones, *op. cit.*, pp. 17-21; Hall, *op. cit.*, p. 107.

ings. The old nonmathematical Aristotelian system gave way in many sciences to one based on the quantitative concepts of mathematics.[10] Beginning in the last quarter of the sixteenth century, one mathematical science and doctrine after the other quickly put in its appearance: analytical trigonometry, decimals, logarithms, analytical geometry, and even the seeds of differential calculus.[11] The sciences of physics, chemistry, physiology, medicine, and botany added vast new data to non-Aristotelian knowledge.[12] Galileo labored to bring experimental and mathematical methods into physics. The substitution of the concept of inertia for the Aristotelian concept of motion posited on a constant addition of energy revolutionized dynamics.[13] The compound microscope, invented by Galileo, was revealing secrets unguessed by the ancients,[14] a complexity of life in lower forms that disturbed the old Aristotelian notions in Browne's favorite biology and in many instances favored the mechanistic theory.[15] The Aristotelian doctrine of spontaneous generation lost ground in the middle of the seventeenth century when maggots were traced to flies, and gall insects to insect eggs.[16]

In the wake of scientific discovery, scientific philosophers— often leading scientists themselves—stimulated research and the revolt from Aristotle. Like the scientists, they fell into two groups, the mathematical and the nonmathematical. Descartes led the mathematicians in their quantitative attack on Aristotle's qualitative system of categories. His theory of the vortices, which long maintained its popularity, undermined the hold of Aristotle's physics. His dualism of nonmaterial soul and mechanical body weakened the grip of Aristotle's teleological interpretation of nature.[17] The teleological question *why* the organism functions as it does had long obscured investigation of

---

[10] J. H. Randall, Jr., "The Development of Scientific Method in the School of Padua," *Journal of the History of Ideas*, I (1940), 180; A. C. Crombie, *Augustine to Galileo; The History of Science A.D. 400-1650* (London, 1952), p. 287.
[11] Singer, *op. cit.*, pp. 189-193, 197.
[12] *Ibid.*, pp. 231-234, 236-242; Dampier-Whetham, *op. cit.*, p. 126.
[13] Crombie, *op. cit.*, p. 289.
[14] Singer, *op. cit.*, p. 217.
[15] *Ibid.*, pp. 243-244.
[16] *Ibid.*, pp. 245-246.
[17] Windelband, *op. cit.*, p. 403.

how it functions, and the work of the seventeenth century was permanently to establish *how* or *how much* as the metaphysical basis of scientific research. Cartesianism made a strong appeal to mid-century Europe and continued its appeal in France throughout the rest of the century. It grew in popular favor in England[18] until its popularity fell off at the end of the century under the onslaught of Newtonian ideas.[19]

The influence of Francis Bacon, prophet of the nonmathematical scientists, began to take effect after 1640, and it determined the scientific climate of England during the rest of the century.[20] Expressing ideas to be echoed again and again throughout the century, Bacon said men are too easily convinced that all truth has been discovered and are too reverent of ancient writers. He attacked Aristotle's meaningless abstractions. Further, Aristotle and the Greeks in general, he said, relied too much upon unwarranted rationalizations about nature and too little upon observation and experiment.[21] For a more satisfactory study of nature, he proposed an application of the recently developed inductive method[22] whereby all the data of nature would be collected and classified and then submitted to a logical process that would result in truth.[23] Whatever the shortcomings of this method and however much he fell short in his practice of it, Bacon was the great advocate for his century in England of experimentation and the new freedom from the bonds of authority. Browne echoes many of his charges against Aristotle and authority in *Pseudodoxia epidemica*.

In his "Salomon's House" of *The New Atlantis*, Bacon had envisioned a group of scientists cooperating to gather data for the benefit of mankind; and, as the mid-century neared, the new science in England developed into a coordinated move-

---

[18] Marjorie Nicolson, "The Early Stage of Cartesianism in England," *Studies in Philology*, XXVI (1929), 356-369. The atomic theory of Pierre Gassendi, friend of Descartes and follower of Bacon, united with similar theories of Galileo and of Descartes to oppose Aristotle's doctrine of forms.
[19] Hall, *op. cit.*, pp. 182, 215-216.
[20] Jones, *op. cit.*, pp. 43, 122.
[21] *Ibid.*, pp. 43-64.
[22] Windelband, *op. cit.*, p. 383.
[23] Singer, *op. cit.*, pp. 226-227; Lynn Thorndike, *A History of Magic and Experimental Science*, 8 vols. (New York, 1923-58), VII, 67-68.

ment.[24] Informal groups began to meet about 1645, and in 1662 the first charter was read to what became the Royal Society.[25] Needless to say, the society was anti-Aristotelian. Its publication *Philosophical Transactions* began in 1665 the modern vogue of scientific papers.[26]

During the sixteenth and seventeenth centuries, the greatest conservative force throughout Europe was the Catholic Church with its intimate ties to Aristotle. To meet the growing challenge, its Council of Trent in 1563 fixed Aristotelian Thomism as the authoritative dogma.[27] Petrus Ramus, a Huguenot professor at the University of Paris who had attacked Aristotle, was forbidden to teach; then three days after the massacre of St. Bartholomew's Day he was murdered[28] for having, as Voltaire puts it, written against Aristotle.[29] For his philosophy as well as his zeal for religious reform, Bruno was brought to the stake in 1600. The seventeenth century witnessed Galileo's punishment by the Inquisition for his contra-Aristotelian discoveries.

The universities had always been strongholds for conservatism and Aristotle, and in general they remained so during most of the seventeenth century.[30] There were two forces for conservatism in the universities: first, the power of the church and, second, the controlling body of opinion within the universities themselves. Since, as will be seen at the end of this introduction, Aristotle made some contribution to seventeenth-century science, conservatism was justified insofar as it was based on that contribution; but the general official attitude meant that a uni-

---

[24] Bacon influenced the movement but did not originate it. Scientific experimental societies existed in France and Italy before the publication in 1627 of *The New Atlantis*. McKie, *op. cit.*, p. 9.

[25] Jones, *op. cit.*, pp. 178-187; McKie, *op. cit.*, pp. 11-36.

[26] Hall, *op. cit.*, p. 203. *Le Journal des Savants* preceded it by two months but ceased publication when announcement came of *Philosophical Transactions*. Maurice Daumas, "La Vie Scientifique au XVIIe Siècle," *XVIIe Siècle*, No. 30 (Jan. 1956), 131.

[27] Windelband, *op. cit.*, p. 363.

[28] Charles Waddington, *Ramus, sa Vie, ses Écrits et ses Opinions* (Paris, 1855), pp. 254-255, 362.

[29] *Ibid.*, p. 256.

[30] Under criticism, Aristotelians tended to dig in behind academic walls. Hall, *op. cit.*, p. 187.

versity scientist might make discoveries that the rest of the university would disapprove. The university deserves credit for providing the scientist with his training and his research opportunity, in spite of his departing from its ruling philosophy, but it can be called a great center of research only with some reservations. The North Italian University of Padua, which was free of political and ecclesiastical domination[31] and which listed among its scientists many of the greatest names of the sixteenth and seventeenth centuries, yet remained loyal to Aristotle.[32] Vesalius was forced to withdraw when he attempted to bring to the classroom what he had learned in the laboratory, and Galileo prudently continued to teach Ptolemaic astronomy.[33] Leyden, like other Dutch universities too recently founded to be determined by tradition, turned out the greatest students of medicine of the century.[34] The Swiss University of Altdorf and the German University of Halle were also exceptional in allowing departures from Aristotle to reach the classroom.[35] All these universities in which some degree of liberalism obtained were municipally controlled. However, in most German universities and in those of France and England, where ecclesiastical rule prevailed, the sciences did not prosper. The University of Montpellier, once in the forefront of liberal medical studies, kept to its now-inadequate lectures and anatomical studies and fell behind in spite of a temporary quickening in the seventeenth century.[36] The University of Paris, under colorful but reactionary leadership, had almost no trace of the new sci-

---

[31] Arturo Castiglioni, "The Medical School at Padua and the Renaissance of Medicine," *Annals of Medical History*, New Ser., VII (1935), 219, 220, 226.

[32] Randall, *op. cit.*, p. 182.

[33] Martha Ornstein, *The Rôle of Scientific Societies in the Seventeenth Century* (Chicago, 1928), p. 218. Browne studied medicine for a time at Padua. It was a Paduan professor who refused on a famous occasion to look through Galileo's telescope lest he see Aristotle refuted.

[34] *Ibid.*, pp. 251-253; Daumas, *op. cit.*, p. 117. It is significant that Browne took his medical degree at Leyden.

[35] Ornstein, *op. cit.*, p. 234.

[36] David Riesman, "The Rise and Early History of Clinical Teaching," *Annals of Medical History*, II (1919), 140-141. Browne began his postgraduate medical studies at Montpellier.

ence in its curriculum;[37] a decree forbade anyone to hold or teach anything against the ancient authors.[38]

Medical instruction at Oxford consisted in little more than the study of the Ancients, especially Aristotle.[39] There was a definite series of fines for disagreeing with him. In 1636 Archbishop Laud, chancellor of Oxford, wrote into law the Stagirite's hold on the curriculum.[40] Because of her great alumnus Bacon, Cambridge acquired a greater reputation for the new science than did Oxford, but astronomy and mathematics were more neglected there than at Oxford during the first half of the century.[41] Isaac Newton, who held the Lucasian professorship from 1669 to 1702, was largely responsible for the association of Cambridge with the new science, but even he for a long time kept his discoveries from his lectures.[42] On the other hand, the English universities deserve some credit for educating members of the Royal Society who were to pass beyond their curricular limitations.[43]

In the latter seventeenth century, opposition to the new science faded in the universities,[44] but in England a reaction set in against Baconian experimentalism, and Aristotle emerged with a victory of sorts. The hangers-on of science had made too many vociferous claims. Besides, serious thinkers had begun to see dangerous implications for religion in the materialism and the mechanical philosophy that sprang out of scientific discoveries,[45] though Newton's formula was eventually to create a new faith in the order of the universe and in the new science.[46] Among the scientists themselves, the first enthusiastic belief

---

[37] Daumas, *op. cit.*, p. 116; Francis R. Packard, *Guy Patin and the Medical Profession in Paris in the XVIIth Century* (New York, 1925), pp. 30, 44-45, 201.
[38] Ornstein, *op. cit.*, pp. 220-226.
[39] R. W. T. Gunther, *Early Science in Oxford*, 14 vols. (Oxford, 1923 [1920]-45), III, 114.
[40] Ornstein, *op. cit.*, p. 237.
[41] William T. Costello, *The Scholastic Curriculum at Early Seventeenth Century Cambridge* (Cambridge, Mass., 1958), p. 102.
[42] Ornstein, *op. cit.*, pp. 247-249.
[43] McKie, *op. cit.*, pp. 33, 35.
[44] Thorndike, *op. cit.*, VII, 640; Hall, *op. cit.*, p. 200.
[45] Jones, *op. cit.*, p. 282.
[46] Thorndike, *op. cit.*, VIII, 604.

that all knowledge could be attained in a generation or two had faded a little, and the hard, ascetic thinking necessary for successful research seemed out of place in an epoch when a handsome leg and the nice set of a powdered wig were paramount considerations. Research was still very much the fashion, but it had fallen into the hands of dabblers, wits, and foplings. Meanwhile, the strong French influence during the Restoration brought to England a sense of the authority of Aristotle's *Poetics* in literary criticism.[47] This new Aristotelian humanism mingled with Cartesian rationalism as part of the background of the neoclassical age of reason. The new science had undermined Aristotelianism, but the crash did not come until the Romantic era.

Before this introduction closes, something should be said in defense of the contribution of Aristotle to seventeenth-century science. Generations succeeding him had established him as a final authority, but he had not so intended, as Sir Thomas Browne was well aware. He had himself set a better example in his preference for truth over his master Plato. Galileo, Jan Baptista van Helmont, and Robert Boyle, who harshly criticized him, were themselves guilty of forgetting this fact and guilty too of ignorance of other facts of scientific history.[48] Whatever his mistakes in astronomy, Aristotle had left in biology an enduring model of observational and experimental science. His biological knowledge was in some areas far superior to anything in the sixteenth century, and even later.[49] Browne had reason to consult him as he did in this the field of his chief interest. The scientists did not universally condemn him. William Harvey did not agree with his spontaneous generation or his position on the importance of blood,[50] but he embraced his vitalist embryological theory of epigenesis, based his doctrine of the circulation of the blood on two of Aristotle's tenets, and

[47] Jones, *op. cit.*, pp. 282-283.
[48] Thorndike, *op. cit.*, VII, 43, 219; VIII, 171; Hall, *op. cit.*, pp. 76, 112.
[49] Hall, *op. cit.*, pp. 134, 156.
[50] Hall, *op. cit.*, p. 154; Walter Pagel, "The Reaction to Aristotle in Seventeenth Century Biological Thought: Campanella, Van Helmont, Glanvill, Charleton, Harvey, Glisson, Descartes," in *Science, Medicine, and History*, ed. E. Ashworth Underwood, 2 vols. (New York, 1953), I, 500.

approved Aristotle's subjection of reason to empiricism.[51] Even
Galileo respected the *Mechanica* (then attributed to Aristotle),
and Van Helmont sided with his vitalism.[52] It has become evident too that Aristotle's logic and physics led to the seventeenth-century scientific method that made Galileo's discoveries possible. Even departures from Aristotle took place within
the Aristotelian framework.[53]

THE WORKS, EDITIONS, AND COMMENTARIES OF ARISTOTLE

In turning to Browne himself, let us consider first what
works and editions of Aristotle interested him as well as the
commentaries on Aristotle that he used. He seems to have read
widely in this most universal of philosophers—in books of biology, physics, meteorology, astronomy, metaphysics, ethics, logic, theology, rhetoric, politics, and literary criticism—but his preoccupations as a physician led him most often to the pages of
the "Books of Animals." In the limited scope of this study, I
have thought it best generally to take my illustrations of his
knowledge and use of Aristotle from these biology books and
other works of science.[54]

Historia animalium, Browne's favorite book of Aristotle, is
mentioned or alluded to in Browne's works much more frequently than any other of Aristotle's books—twenty times un-

---

[51] *Ibid.,* pp. 501, 507, 499, 502-503; Crombie, *op. cit.,* p. 385.

[52] Thorndike, *op. cit.,* VII, 43; Pagel, *op. cit.,* I, 507-508.

[53] Randall, *op. cit.,* pp. 180, 184, 203, 206.

[54] Since this study is concerned principally with Browne as a scholar of
Aristotle, for studies concerned in part with Browne's philosophical apprehension of Aristotle's theories of reproduction, classification of plants, psychology, and logic, see Egon Stephen Merton, *Science and Imagination in
Sir Thomas Browne* (New York, 1949), pp. 21, 42 ff, 52, 58, 69, 70, 77-78;
also, articles by the same author: "Sir Thomas Browne's Scientific Quest,"
Journal of the History of Medicine, III (1948), 214-228; "Sir Thomas
Browne's Interpretation of Dreams," *Philological Quarterly,* XXVIII
(1949), 497-503; "Sir Thomas Browne's Embryological Theory," *Journal
of the History of Medicine,* V (1950), 416-421; "The Botany of Sir Thomas
Browne," *Isis,* XLVII (1956), 161-171; and "Microcosm, Epitome, and Seed:
Some Seventeenth-Century Analogies," *History of Ideas News Letter,* III
(1957), 54-57. H. MacL. Currie, "Notes on Sir Thomas Browne's 'Christian
Morals,'" *Notes and Queries,* New Ser., V (1958), 143, offers philosophical
sources in Aristotle's *De caelo* and *Ethica Nicomachea.*

mistakably;[55] and it is included in the vague sweep of "Books of Animals" three times besides.[56] Seventy-six informational references and allusions have their definite source in *Historia animalium*;[57] and five others have their chief likely source in this work.[58] In addition, forty passages in Browne find in *Historia animalium* good possible sources and what I call *passim* sources.[59] The latter term designates two or more highly probable sources of equal probability. These possible and *passim* sources often are numerous since Aristotle tends to be repetitive.

"[Aristotelis] *Histor. de Animalib. gr. lat. cum Comment. Scaligeri* 1619." Thus is indicated in the sale catalogue, *A Catalogue of the Libraries of the Learned Sir Thomas Brown, and Dr. Edward Brown, His Son* (London, 1711), p. 19, item 91, Browne's weighty volume of *Historia animalium*, edited by Julius Caesar Scaliger,[60] great scholar father of a great son, Joseph Justus Scaliger, and a thorough Latinist and Aristotelian,

---

[55] The principal edition of Browne to be used in this study is *The Works of Sir Thomas Browne*, ed. Geoffrey Keynes, 6 vols. (London, 1928-31). The other edition, *Sir Thomas Browne's Works, Including His Life and Correspondence*, ed. Simon Wilkin, 4 vols. (London, 1835-36), will be used as necessary for its footnotes and for material not in the Keynes edition. The Keynes edition will be designated K, and the Wilkin edition, W. Subsequent references to these editions will appear in the text whenever feasible. The references and allusions to *Historia animalium*: K, II, 187, 207; K, V, 50, 239, 258 (bis), 270, 306, 316, 362; K, VI, 65, 135, 146 (bis), 149, 177, 182, 210, 220; W, IV, 298. A large proportion of these references are in the Letters and Commonplace Books.

[56] K, II, 44, 57; K, III, 75. The quotation varies slightly in form.

[57] For brevity, I shall give only those in the first two volumes of the Keynes edition: K, I, 188 (518^{b}19), 188 (518^{b}25); K, II, 53 (584^{b}1), 57 (501^{a}24, 606^{a}7), 57 (523^{a}26), 167 (617^{a}18), 179 (498^{a}8), 187-188 (506^{b}20), 206-207 (578^{b}23), 208-209 (611^{a}31), 209-210 (606^{a}7), 220 (616^{a}7), 231 (552^{b}15), 236 (532^{a}3), 237 (558^{a}28), 248 (585^{a}12), 249 (579^{b}16), 250-252 (491^{b}28), 253 (532^{a}5), 256 (491^{b}26), 258 (503^{a}15), 270 (605^{a}26), 285 (564^{a}4), 295 574^{a}20), 298 (535^{b}4), 299 (604^{b}18).

[58] K, II, 249 (539^{b}22); K, III, 195 (546^{b}11), 253 (524^{b}14); K, V, 301 (492^{a}31); K, VI, 90 (520^{a}6).

[59] Those in the first two volumes of the Keynes edition: K, I, 20 (546^{b}15); K, II, 89 (523^{a}19), 173 (546^{b}15), 179 (498^{a}8), 184-186 (506^{a}22), 196-197 (579^{a}21), 211 (506^{a}21), 224 (517^{b}7, 538^{a}2, 569^{a}5, 570^{a}3), 224-225 (546^{b}15), 227 (519^{b}13, 541^{a}3), 247 (542^{b}32), 249 (579^{a}30, 579^{b}30), 250-252 (533^{a}2), 253 (534^{b}15), 256 (535^{a}5), 302 (546^{b}15).

[60] The title, as listed in the catalogue of the British Museum, is *Aristotelis Historia de animalibus; Iulio Caesare Scaligero interprete, cum eiusdem commentarijs* (Toulouse, 1619).

who, aware of his own greatness, often disagrees with, even heckles, his master and who rubricates his passages of commentary, three or four times as long as the text, with the significant "Caesar." "This book," says Browne, "I beleeve is not common; myne was printed at Tholosae 1619 in a fayre letter, Greek & Latin, & I think it was never reprinted since, being somewhat a thick folio" (K, VI, 149). Browne refers to this text and its commentary probably more often than to any other edition of any other author—thirty-four times.[61] With varying degrees of adherence to his text, he quotes Scaliger's translation of Aristotle twenty-one times,[62] and he quotes the commentary, with all sorts of textual variations, seventeen times.[63]

In addition to Scaliger's translation of *Historia animalium*, Browne had the Latin translation of Theodore Gaza. It is not listed in the sale catalogue, and evidence is lacking to connect Browne with any particular edition of this often-reprinted translation. The 1476 edition (Venice), for one, also contains Gaza's translation of *De partibus animalium* and of *De generatione animalium*,[64] but we cannot prove that Browne had this or a similar edition and so read *De partibus* and *De generatione* in Gaza's translation.

Browne refers to Gaza's *Historia animalium* comparatively seldom,[65] and quotes it in almost every instance.[66] He only once quotes Gaza's version independently of Scaliger's (K, II, 187). Twice he prefers Scaliger's version to Gaza's;[67] once he quotes the two versions together without making a decision between them (K, II, 251); and once he takes Gaza's version instead of Scaliger's—though with some misgivings—because Gaza's version alone suits his purposes (K, I, 188). He evidently prefers

---

[61] K, I, 188; K, II, 199-200, 206-207, 220, 226, 232, 241, 249, 250-251, 298; K, III, 14, 26-27, 50, 75-76, 223; K, IV, 66; K, V, 75, 258 (three times), 306, 316, 328; K, VI, 135, 141, 143, 146, 149, 175, 177, 182, 210, 220-221; W, IV, 298.

[62] K, II, 207, 220, 231, 241, 249, 251; K, III, 223, 253; K, V, 258, 306, 318, 342; K, VI, 135, 141, 146, 149, 175, 177, 182, 220-221; W, IV, 298.

[63] K, II, 226; K, III, 134; K, V, 258 (bis), 306, 316, 328; K, VI, 135, 141, 143, 146, 149, 175, 177, 182, 210, 221.

[64] *Nouvelle Biographie Générale*, ed. Firmin Didot frères, 46 vols. (Paris, 1853-66), XIX, 777. For another Gaza edition, see note 133.

[65] Four times: K, I, 188; K, II, 241, 251; K, III, 223.

[66] K, II, 241, 251; K, III, 223.

[67] K, II, 241; K, III, 223.

Scaliger to Gaza, possibly because Gaza has no commentary and was frequently printed without the Greek original. Gaza generally comes to his hand only when there is some question.

Three Latin quotations from *Historia animalium* found in Browne differ widely from the Scaliger and Gaza versions, and search for another translation of *Historia animalium* that might agree with two of these has proved fruitless.[68] Browne had at least one Greek text of the work—the text in Scaliger—and he quotes the Greek very frequently, paralleling it with the Latin of Scaliger or Gaza, and checking their versions by his own knowledge of Greek. Very likely Browne is yielding here to his fondness, demonstrated elsewhere, for making his own Latin versions. The probability is increased in these instances by the facts that one of these quotations represents a telescoping of the Greek sources[69] and that the other purports to be a literal translation of the Greek that Scaliger had refused to make since it would have exposed Aristotle's folly (K, III, 50).

None of the other four "Books of Animals," as Browne calls them, appear in the sale catalogue, though Browne read all, or nearly all, of them. Quite likely they were given away between the date of Browne's death, 1682, and the date of the sale, 1711,[70] or were kept by the female line of the family, which survived after 1711. Of these four works, Browne mentions by name only two: *De motu animalium*, once (in this mention he couples the work with its associate piece as "*De motu aut incessu animalium*") (K, VI, 232), and *De incessu animalium*, three times by itself,[71] one of these times with approval as an "excellent Tract" (K, III, 25). He covers *De generatione animalium* and *De partibus animalium* only with the blanket designation "Book [or "Books"] of Animals,"[72] which is twice lengthened to "through all his Book [or "Books"] of Animals," words apparently indicating that he has read them all. *De generatione animalium, De partibus animalium,* and *De incessu ani-*

---

[68] K, II, 241; K, III, 50; K, V, 239. The quotation beginning "Parit autem ..." (K, II, 241) is obviously, from the context, Browne's own translation.
[69] K, V, 239.
[70] Suggested by R. R. Cawley, "Sir Thomas Browne and His Reading," *PMLA*, XLVIII (1933), 429.
[71] K, II, 179, 195; K, III, 25.
[72] K, II, 44, 57; K, III, 75.

malium, each supplies from three to six definite sources for references in Browne.[73] In addition, *De generatione* supplies chief likely sources for four Browne passages and possible and *passim* sources for twenty-nine passages;[74] *De partibus,* chief likely sources for two passages; and *De incessu,* one chief likely source.[75] It is clear that Browne read these three works, the short *De incessu* apparently with special attention. In spite of his coupling of its title with the title of *De incessu,* and the twice-stated inclusive "through all his Book [or "Books"] of Animals," *De motu animalium* has only a single alternative source to indicate that he read it (K, II, 179 [703ª20]). He may not have read it at all.

I have no evidence about the editions and commentaries of the animal books other than *Historia animalium,* except a slight clue in this statement about the ostrich: "For Aristotle and Oppianus who have particularly treated hereof are silent in this singularity; either omitting it as dubious, or as the Comment saith, rejecting it as fabulous" (K, II, 268). If the "Comment" referred to is a commentary on Aristotle, it must be a commentary on *De partibus animalium,* for Aristotle has "particularly treated" the ostrich only in that work; and this clue could mean that Browne's edition of *De partibus* was equipped with commentary. It is possible, as I have suggested earlier, that Browne possessed Gaza's *De partibus* and *De generatione* bound in, as was often the case, with *Historia animalium.*

Browne treats *Problemata,* the great collection of problems in natural science, with a scholarly definiteness not usual with

---

[73] *De generatione:* K, II, 57 (736ª2), 234-235 (773ª8), 235 (770ª24), 246 (772b27); K, III, 25 (765ª21), 309 (718ª23); *De partibus:* K, II, 211 (677ª30), 268 (697b14); K, III, 134 (663ª19); *De incessu:* K, II, 179 (709ª9), 179 (704b22), 196 (712ª24); K, III, 25-26 (705ª26).

[74] Chief likely sources: K, I, 46 (736b27); K, II, 224 (762b22), 247 (774ª30); K, III, 24-25 (763b30); possible and *passim* sources for passages in the first two volumes of the Keynes edition: K, I, 20 (761ª12, 761b24), 20 (744ª36, 744b16), 45 (736b27); K, II, 82-83 (727ª26, 727b6, 727b34, 729ª9, 729ª21, 730ª24, 732ª7, 739ª20), 89 (735ª34), 173 (761ª12, 761b24), 196 (774b25), 224 (741ª39), 224 (761ª12, 761b24), 224-225 (761ª12, 761b24), 235 (776b11), 246 (727ª26, 727b6, 727b34, 729ª9, 729ª21, 730ª24, 732ª7, 739ª20), 261 (784ª34), 302 (761ª12, 761b24).

[75] *De partibus:* K, II, 184-186 (676b26, 677ª30); K, III, 26-27 (684ª25); *De incessu:* K, VI, 77-78 (712ª10).

him. This work, Aristotle's only in part, appears in the sale catalogue, and Browne mentions it by name or in some unmistakable fashion seventeen times[76]—almost as many times as *Historia animalium*. One hundred and forty references and citations find definite sources in the thirty-eight books of *Problemata*, and nineteen in addition have sources there of varying degrees of probability.[77] Only the fact that Browne concentrates a large proportion of the many references to *Problemata* in a comparatively few pages of his own writing prevents the conclusion that he favored this work over *Historia animalium*.

In his posthumously published "Notae in Aristotelem" (in Latin; W, IV, 360-366) Browne speaks in rather disparaging terms of three men who have worked on *Problemata*: Petrus Aponensis, Alexander Aphrodisaeus, and "Petrus" Septalius.[78] By his use of the word "illustraverunt," he evidently means that these three men have written commentaries. In editions of *Problemata* available to Browne the commentary of Petrus Aponensis, or Petrus de Abano, is coupled with a translation of *Problemata* by Theodore Gaza.[79] Browne makes one other reference besides the one in "Notae in Aristotelem" to the commentary of Petrus (K, II, 294); however, none of his Latin quotations agree with the Gaza text that accompanies the commentary. Alexander Aphrodisaeus, or Aphrodisiensis, is author of two books of problems resembling those of Aristotle, his mas-

---

[76] K, I, 173; K, II, 44, 146, 294; K, III, 10, 22, 41 (marginal note), 41, 42, 47, 232, 298, 300, 303; K, VI, 228, 229; W, IV, 360.

[77] Definite sources for references and citations in the six volumes of the Keynes edition (omitting, for brevity, definite sources for the extended treatment in W, IV, 360-366, and all possible and *passim* sources): K, I, 173 (891^a8); K, II, 44 (891^a8), 44 (895^b12), 44 (898^a31), 146 (938^b25), 294 (937^b38); K, III, 9-10 (892^b15), 41 (962^a35), 41 (962^b19), 42 (907^b35), 47 (908^b11), 54-55 (910^b24), 232 (967^b1), 233 (966^b20), 298 (879^a15), 298 (931^a35–936^a10), 300 (940^a2), 303 (950^a1); K, V, 227 (962^a1); K, VI, 229 (938^a23), 229 (938^b5), 229 (941^a20), 229 (942^a5), 229 (942^a16), 229 (942^a22), 229 (942^a29), 229 (942^b3), 229 (945^a13), 229 (945^a26), 229 (945^a28), 229 (945^b5), 229 (946^a4), 229 (947^a25), 229 (947^a28).

[78] W, IV, 360. Under the influence of "Petrus Aponensis," Browne calls Ludovicus Septalius "Petrus Septalius."

[79] Copy in Harvard University Library: "*Aristotelis Problemata T. Gaza interprete cum Expositione Petri de Abano. Impresa p. me Paulum Johannis de puzpach. Almanum Magontinensis Dyocesis, Mantue, 1475.*" This is listed in *Nouvelle Biographie Générale*, ed. Firmin Didot frères, 46 vols. (Paris, 1853-66), I, 30.

ter. They frequently appeared in Latin translation from the Greek with the *Problemata* of Aristotle, as in a Gaza edition of 1524 listed in the catalogue of the British Museum.[80] A reprint of this is probably one of the two editions of *Problemata* mentioned in the sale catalogue: "*Aristotelis Problemata, Latine ...Par. 1562.*"[81] The catalogue of the British Museum shows no other Latin edition than this between 1539 and the 1570's. There is no evidence of Browne's using Alexander's work; indeed, his words in "Notae in Aristotelem" suggest that he thought it a commentary on *Problemata*, as of course it is not.

The edition of *Problemata* that did service for Browne is the great folio volume of Ludovicus Septalius, with Greek text and Septalius' Latin translation and commentary, although Browne echoes elsewhere the disparagement that appears in "Notae in Aristotelem": "Aristotles problems in Greek and Latin were published in folio with a large comment of Ludovicus Septalius the physitian. Hee was a learned man, butt some philosophers of this present time might give a cleerer solution of many of them" (K, VI, 229). The work appears in the sale catalogue as "*Aristotelis Problemata, gr. lat. cum Lud. Septalii Comment. 1632.*"[82] With allowance for typical alterations by Browne, this translation supplies the source of Browne's quotations from *Problemata*.

Meteorologica, the work concerned principally with the weather phenomena that its name now covers, is listed in the sale catalogue; and it is mentioned in Browne's works—whether in text or marginal notes—nine times, generally as "*Meteors.*"[83] Eleven references in Browne have their definite source in *Meteorologica* and four their chief likely source.[84] As with *Prob-*

---

[80] *General Catalogue of Printed Books* (London, 1931-), VI, 198: "*Problematum Aristotelis sectiones duae de quadraginta: Theodoro Gaza interprete. Problematum Alexandri Aphrodisiei libri duo: eodem Theodoro interprete ... Parisiis, 1524.*"

[81] P. 27, item 61.

[82] P. 19, item 90. The title, as listed in the catalogue of the British Museum, is *Ludovici Septalii ... in Aristotelis Problemata commentaria, ab eo Latinè facta....*, 3 vols. (Lyons, 1632).

[83] K, II, 44, 151, 310; K, III, 216, 249, 298, 306; K, IV, 91 (marginal note); K, VI, 342 (marginal note).

[84] Definite sources: K, II, 44 (383^{b}13), 90 (382^{b}28), 310 (348^{a}33); K, III, 216 (353^{a}1), 249 (387^{a}23), 298 (353^{a}27–359^{b}25), 306 (359^{a}17); K, IV, 91

lemata, Browne, in employing information from *Meteorologica,* almost invariably refers to the work by name.

Browne makes it clear that he has the Greek text of *Meteorologica,*[85] more than one translation,[86] and more than one commentary.[87] Twice he refers to the Latin edition with commentary of Nicolo Cabeo—once referring to the text[88] and once to the commentary (K, II, 95). The commentary of "Cabeus" he calls an "excellent discourse of Meteors." This work appears in the sale catalogue: *"Nic. Cabei Aristotelis Comment. 2 Vol. . . . Rom. 1646."*[89] Actually this edition is in four volumes.[90] Two of the four volumes had evidently disappeared from the Browne library by the time of the sale. Browne refers once to a Vicomercatus edition of *Meteorologica* with commentary, and his reference to it leaves no doubt of his having had it (K, III, 298). Two editions of Franciscus Vicomercatus, either of which may be Browne's, are listed in the catalogue of the British Museum.[91] There is no entry for it in the sale catalogue.

Physica is mentioned in "Notae in Aristotelem" in a tone of depreciation: "physica parum teris" (W, IV, 360). Three definite sources are located in this work and two chief likely sources.[92] There is no evidence to connect Browne with any particular edition or translation.

De caelo, the work dealing with the movement of heavenly and terrestrial bodies, is mentioned by name only once (K, III, 160). Evidence favors the identification of *De caelo* with the work mentioned in *Religio medici* as "an imperfect piece of Philosophy" that might have been "an absolute tract of

---

(380^a11); K, V, 206 (355^b33); K, VI, 342 (352^a3), 350-351 (352^a28); chief likely sources: K, III, 216 (352^b20), 216 (350^a23); K, VI, 343 (352^b20), 349 (352^b20).

[85] K, III, 249, 306; K, VI, 351.

[86] K, III, 306: " . . . second of his *Meteors* . . . ὥσπερ μυθολογοῦσι, which word is variously rendred, by some as a fabulous account, by some as a common talk."

[87] K, VI, 351: " . . . allowed by his comentators . . . "

[88] K, IV, 91 (marginal note).

[89] P. 19, item 92.

[90] Catalogue of the British Museum, VI, 119.

[91] VI, 118-119. One edition, in Greek and Latin, appeared in 1556 and was reprinted in 1598; the other, in Latin, appeared in 1565.

[92] Definite sources: K, I, 21 (193^a30), 21 (192^b12), 24-26 $(198^a1—199^a8)$. Chief likely sources: K, I, 19 (194^b16); K, II, 52 $(187^a20—192^b5)$.

Divinity" had Aristotle inquired more deeply into the final cause.[93] There are two definite sources, one chief likely source, and a host of possible sources in *De caelo*.[94]

I have no evidence about the text of *De caelo*; however, Browne used Simplicius' commentary on it, which contains scraps of Aristotle's text (which form the basis for the comment). Browne says:

> For as Simplicius relateth, Aristotle required of Calisthenes, who accompanied that Worthy [Alexander] in his Expedition, that at his arrive at Babylon, he would enquire of the antiquity of their Records; and those upon compute he found to amount unto 1903 years; which account notwithstanding ariseth no higher than 95 years after the flood. (K, III, 162-163.)

In a modern edition of Simplicius the figure is not "1903" but "11003."[95] In Browne's time the generally available version of Simplicius' commentary on *De caelo* was a Latin translation from Simplicius' Greek by Gulielmus de Morbeka, who lived in the thirteenth century. A Greek version was available at the time but it was not the original Greek of Simplicius, which was not obtainable until the latter part of the nineteenth century; it was a translation from the Latin of Gulielmus.[96] In the Latin

---

[93] K, I, 20. The reference to "Suarez' Metaphysicks" in the preceding sentence might have reminded Browne of Aristotle's *Metaphysica*, and the "causes" are taken up in *Metaphysica*, not in *De caelo*. On the other hand, Browne is looking for a "tract of Divinity" and his disappointment would naturally fall upon *De caelo*. In the second sentence above, he says: "In the causes, nature and affections of the Eclipses of the Sun and Moon, there is most excellent speculation; but to profound farther, and to contemplate a reason why his Providence hath so disposed and ordered their motions in that vast circle as to conjoyn and obscure each other, is a sweeter piece of Reason, and a diviner point of Philosophy." In a passage through which Aristotle stalks from beginning to end, this is a description of the contents, and, from Browne's point of view, the failings of just one work of Aristotle: *De caelo*.

[94] I shall give only the definite and chief likely sources. Definite sources: K, I, 20 (291^{b}29); K, II, 151 (289^{a}21). Chief likely source: K, I, 44-45 (276^{a}18).

[95] *Simplicii in Aristotelis De caelo commentaria*, ed. I. L. Heiberg (Berlin, 1894), p. 506, line 14. Literally, the Greek is to be translated "one thousand and ten thousand and three"; quite likely the figure "1903" in the translations is an attempt to emend an obvious error in the original.

[96] *Nouvelle Biographie Générale*, XLIV, 30. For the edition of original Greek, see note 95 *supra*.

versions of Gulielmus and the Greek version stemming from it, the figure is "1903."[97] There is no way of telling whether Browne used the Greek version or the Latin. Both were published in Venice in reverse order of their origin, the Greek in 1526, the Latin in 1540.[98]

De generatione et corruptione, the small companion piece to *De caelo*, is not mentioned by Browne. Since it offers only four alternative sources for one Browne passage,[99] there is no real case for Browne's having read it. The alternative sources probably reflect Aristotle's bent for repetition of material. There is no evidence pointing to a particular edition or commentary.

This concludes the consideration of Aristotle's works in biology and the other sciences, or at least those works that seem to be wholly or in part authentically Aristotle's. Browne mentions two additional works, both now regarded as apocryphal, the first of which is biological and the second partly so: *De plantis*[100] and *De mirabilibus auscultationibus*. There are one definite source and two alternative sources in *De plantis*, but only one *passim* source in *De mirabilibus*.[101] Browne seems to be stating his own practice when he says of the latter that it "may be read with caution."[102]

There is no evidence to connect any particular edition of *De plantis* or *De mirabilibus* with Browne, but he clearly used Scaliger's commentary on *De plantis*. It appears in the sale catalogue,[103] and Browne mentions Scaliger's comment on the

[97] Simplicius, *ed. cit.*, p. 506, n.
[98] *Nouvelle Biographie Générale*, XLIV, 30.
[99] K, I, 97 (315ᵃ29, 315ᵇ25, 329ᵃ13, 335ᵇ8).
[100] *De plantis* is mentioned in "Musaeum Clausum" (K, V, 134) and in the 1646 and 1650 editions of *Pseudodoxia* (Bk. II, chap. 6; same passage as K, II, 161).
[101] *De plantis*, definite source: K, II, 161 (816ᵇ40); alternative sources: K, II, 161 (815ᵃ18, 817ᵃ40). *De mirabilibus, passim* source: K, V, 71 (841ᵇ15). For the latter Browne uses a synonymous title: *De mirandis auditionibus*.
[102] In *Pseudodoxia*, Bk. I, chap. 8, headed "Of Authors who have most promoted Popular Conceit": "There is a book *De mirandis auditionibus*, ascribed unto Aristotle . . . [which] may be read with caution." (W, II, 236); with different chapter title, K, II, 58.
[103] P. 23, item 38: "*J. C. Scaligeri in Aristotelem de Plantis libri duo Marp.* 1598."

definite-source passage in *De plantis*.[104] Scaliger's publication does not include the text of Aristotle. In "Musaeum Clausum" Browne speaks of "King Alfred upon *Aristotle de Plantis*," presumably a book he has heard of, would like to see, and never has seen (K, V, 134). This version of *De plantis* was translated from the Arabic by Alfredus de Sareshel at the end of the twelfth or beginning of the thirteenth century. Known as "Alfredus Anglicus," the translator was often confused with another "Alfredus Anglicus" of the late thirteenth century and often with King Alfred, who was also known as "Alfredus Anglicus." In fact, *De educatione accipitrum*, possibly by King Alfred, has sometimes mistakenly been ascribed to Alfredus de Sareshel or the other Alfredus.[105]

Evidence of varying degrees of probability connects Browne with other works of Aristotle. Since they are outside the scope of this study, I shall simply list them. The philosophical works are *Metaphysica* and *De mundo*, the latter of which is apocryphal. The psychological works are *De anima, De sensu et sensibili, De somno et vigilia, De divinatione per somnum*, and *De respiratione*. The ethical works are *Ethica Nicomachea, Ethica Eudemia, Magna moralia*, and *De virtutibus et vitiis* (apocryphal). The logical works to be connected with Browne are *Analytica priora, Analytica posteriora, Topica*, and *De sophisticis elenchis*. The remaining works for which there is evidence that Brown read or may have read them are miscellaneous: *Physiognomonica* (apocryphal), *Mechanica* (apocryphal), *De lineis insecabilibus* (probably apocryphal), *De melisso* (apocryphal), *De Xenophane* (apocryphal), *De Gorgia* (apocryphal), *Politica, Rhetorica, Theologica* (apocryphal), and *Poetica*. Of the works listed in this paragraph, *De anima, Ethica Nicomachea, De sophisticis elenchis, Physiognomonica*, and *Politica* are the only ones to supply Browne with three or more definite sources, though *Physiognomonica* and *Politica* supply the re-

---

[104] See note 101 *supra*.

[105] S. D. Wingate, *The Mediaeval Latin Versions of the Aristotelian Scientific Corpus with Special Reference to the Biological Works* (London, 1931), pp. 55-58. *De educatione accipitrum*, also known as *De accipitribus*, is no longer extant.

markable number of eight.[106] There is not space enough to allow information on the editions and commentaries of the works listed here. Browne's main interest lies in biology and the other sciences.

Four other works are mentioned by Browne, most of which he makes clear he has never read, never having been able to obtain them: "*De Lapide*";[107] "a Work of the propriety of Elements, ascribed unto Aristotle: which notwithstanding is not reputed genuine";[108] "*de Precationibus*";[109] and the poetry of Aristotle.[110] The following works, authentic and apocryphal, do

---

[106] *De anima*: K, I, 16 (414ᵇ30), 61 (419ᵃ12); K, II, 115 (405ᵃ20). *Ethica Nicomachea*: K, I, 95 (1130ᵃ14), 107 (1125ᵃ5); K, III, 302 (1100ᵃ10). *De sophisticis elenchis*: K, II, 32-33 (165ᵇ23), 35 (166ᵇ20), 35 (167ᵃ37), 35-36 (166ᵇ38), 36-37 (167ᵇ20), 37 (167ᵇ1). *Physiognomonica*: K, V, 5 (811ᵇ33), 252 (810ᵃ15), 252 (810ᵇ7), 252 (811ᵃ10), 252 (812ᵃ9), 253 (808ᵃ34), 253 (808ᵃ12), 290-291 (808ᵃ12). *Politica*: K, II, 46 (1326ᵃ15); K, III, 27 (1274ᵇ-12), 62 (1316ᵃ1), 101 (1336ᵇ19), 211 (1330ᵃ38), 303 (1342ᵇ8); K, IV, 74 (1330ᵇ29); K, V, 246-247 (1326ᵃ15).

[107] K, II, 112. "On the Magnet, one book" appears in the list of Aristotle's works given by Diogenes Laërtius, third-century Greek biographer, in *Lives of Eminent Philosophers*, trans. R. D. Hicks, 2 vols. (Loeb Classical Library, New York, 1925), I, 473. This list was familiar to Browne (see note 110 *infra*). Under "doubtful or supposititious works" of Aristotle, the catalogue of the British Museum lists (VI, 189) items "*De Lapide Philosophico*" and "*De Lapidibus*."

[108] K, III, 298. A work "on Elements, three books" appears in the list of Diogenes Laërtius (*op. cit.*, I, 467). Under "doubtful or supposititious works" of Aristotle, the catalogue of the British Museum (VI, 187) lists: "*Secreta secretorum Aristotelis . . . de signis aquarum ventorum et tempestatum . . . de mineralibus . . . Parisiis*, 1520."

[109] K, V, 134. The full title of the tract in which this title appears indicates the extent of Browne's personal acquaintance with *De precationibus*: "Musaeum Clausum, or Bibliotheca Abscondita: Containing Some Remarkable Books, Antiquities, Pictures & Rarities of Several Kinds, Scarce or Never Seen by Any Man Now Living." K, V, 131. Περὶ εὐχῆς (Of Prayer) appears in the list of Aristotle's works given by Hesychius of Miletus, Greek biographer of the sixth century, *Aristotelis qui ferebantur librorum fragmenta collegit Valentinus Rose* (Leipzig, 1886), p. 11. The source for Browne was undoubtedly the Diogenes Laërtius (*op. cit.*, I, 465) he read so often.

[110] W, IV, 300. In "Nonnulla a lectione Athenaei scripta," in which he makes clear that his source for Aristotle's titles is Diogenes Laërtius, Browne laments the loss of Aristotle's poetry: "Utinam vel sub quovis nomine superesset pars aliquotula librorum Aristotelis, quos expes lego relegoque in Catalogo Laertiano; fertur et vir summus nonnihil in poesin retulisse, quam ego certe poesi Ciceroniana non gravate redimerem." *Ibid.* The last two items in the list of Diogenes Laërtius (*op. cit.*, I, 475) are poems.

not appear in the sale catalogue, are not mentioned by Browne, and do not supply so much as one alternative source: *Categoriae, De interpretatione, Oeconomica, Atheniensium respublica, De rhetorica ad Alexandrum, De coloribus, De audibilibus, Ventorum situs et cognomine, De memoria et reminiscentia, De somniis, De longitudine et brevitate vitae, De iuventute et senectute, De vita et morte,* and *De spiritu.*

THE TREASURE HOUSE OF FACTS

When Browne turned to Aristotle's works, certain materials interested him more than others. His religion impelled him to study Aristotle's philosophy, but his medical training and practice, as well as the subjects chosen for study in *Pseudodoxia epidemica*, made him turn more frequently to Aristotle the treasure house of factual lore than to Aristotle the philosopher.[111] Few of the factual references to Aristotle are not from some field of science such as biology, physics, astronomy, geology, or physiography—a fact rendered perhaps the more natural by Aristotle's having done most of his factual work in those fields.

It is in biology that Aristotle makes his greatest contribution to Browne, who consults him on one or more forms in every important order of animals from the snail of the molluscan phylum to man of the order of primates. Aristotle's regional limitations and his lack of the microscope prevented research on animals very far below the Mollusca, though he does treat certain lower forms which he calls zoophytes, half animal and half plant.[112] Of the five hundred animals that Aristotle mentions, Browne consults him on fifty-one.[113]

Browne's references to Aristotle's data on the lower animals are few and glancing. He is interested in Aristotle's statement that testaceans, consequently snails, have no eyes (K, II, 256); that, lacking sex, they cannot generate (K, II, 224); and that

---

[111] Cf. Peter Green, *Sir Thomas Browne* (booklet in "Bibliographical Series of Supplements to 'British Book News' on Writers and Their Work," No. 108) (London, 1959), p. 27.

[112] W. D. Ross, *Aristotle* (London, 1930), pp. 116-117.

[113] Here Aristotle's material will be given as Browne represents it; the question of Browne's accuracy is treated elsewhere.

cuttlefish discharge a "black humour" (K, III, 253). Above these Mollusca are the crustaceans. Here are references to the enlarged right claw of crabs and lobsters (K, III, 26-27) and the ventless hermit crab (K, V, 342). Of the arachnids, the Scolopendra may crawl backward or forward (K, II, 236), and spiders cast off their skin many times annually (K, VI, 80). References increase with the insects. All flying insects have eyes though possibly no other sensory organs (K, II, 253). The cicada has no mouth (K, III, 93-94). 'Ακρίς refers to the familiar locust (K, III, 285). The grape beetle kills the animal that swallows it (K, II, 299). Bees visit only one kind of flower on each trip (K, V, 332). Contact between the "con-natural spirit" and the membrane of the thorax produces the humming of insects (K, II, 298). Thus far the references are scattered and lack the detailed treatment that Aristotle gives to some of these animals, notably the bee.

Fish with fins and scales have arenaceous eggs (K, III, 45). Tunny and mackerel pair in February and spawn in June (K, III, 223). Eels, lacking sex, do not generate (K, II, 224); and when dead do not float because they lack fat (K, III, 31-32). The "*Acus*" is a needlefish resembling a snake (K, V, 399; K, VI, 368). Speaking of amphibians, Aristotle seems to think that the salamander can live in fire and extinguish it (K, II, 231). He says nothing about the reptile chameleon's living on air alone (K, II, 258). There is a serpent with a head at each end (K, II, 235). If the tail of a snake is cut off, a new tail will grow (K, V, 306). Aristotle and his commentators seem to believe that vipers come to birth by tearing through the abdomen of their mother (K, II, 237, 241). There is no mention in him of the mythical basilisk (K, II, 199), and no oviparous animal urinates except the tortoise (K, II, 227).

Aristotle does not mention the ostrich's digesting iron (K, II, 268) or the pelican's opening her breast to feed her young with her blood (K, III, 89). He commends the flesh of young hawks (K, II, 285), but, ignorant of falconry, he has hawks refusing to eat the hearts of birds (K, V, 75). Aristotle's hawks cannot be reconciled with ours, according to Scaliger (K, V, 75). Hawks and other birds of prey do not drink (K, V, 76).

Here we have several references on one subject, on the hawk, a subject on which Browne knows himself to be better informed than Aristotle. Aristotle says the buzzard has three testicles (K, II, 234); and the crow, swallow, sparrow, and dove have the gall attached to the intestines (K, II, 187). Aristotle mentions a mistle thrush that feeds upon mistletoe (K, II, 167), and a "*Cinnamomus*" that builds its nest of cinnamon (K, II, 220). The variegation of birds is due to their living in the sun (K, III, 298).

The references grow more numerous as we ascend the class of the Mammalia. Moles have eyes but no sight (K, II, 250, 251). Hares may conceive during pregnancy (K, II, 247), and they copulate aversely (K, III, 133-134). In order to escape the hunter, the beaver bites off his testicles (K, II, 66, 190). Animals that split the hoof also double the horn (K, III, 134). Syrian sheep have tails a cubit broad (K, V, 50). The drinking water of sheep can influence the color of their wool (K, III, 238). The camel has no gall bladder (K, II, 211). The boar is not to be found in Africa (K, II, 210), and the hogs of Illyria are whole-footed (K, III, 241). With cattle the number of references per animal greatly increases. Oxen and cows do not cough (K, I, 173; K, II, 44), and oxen do not belch (K, II, 44). One must anoint the horns to treat hoof diseases of oxen (K, V, 258). The shepherd must stand to milk the great cows of Epirus (K, VI, 221). A bull may continue to generate for some time after castration (K, III, 25). The blood of bulls is thick, dark, and fibrous (K, VI, 149, 175).

The deer is treated in some detail. In a letter to his son Edward, Sir Thomas lists material on the deer from *Historia animalium* and Julius Scaliger's commentary: the deer has a very large heart but nonfibrous blood, intestines so tender that they break at a blow even though the hide is not broken, and a keener sense of hearing when its ears are erect than when they are drooping; and it has worms in the head (K, VI, 175). Many references to the deer are found elsewhere. The deer has no gall (K, II, 211), and in old age it loses certain antlers and its teeth (K, II, 208-209). The ears of the "Arginusa" deer are slit (K, III, 239). The short gestation of the deer and its quick maturity argue against its great longevity (K, II, 206-207). It is not to be found in Africa (K, II, 210).

The number of references drops with the odd-toed ungulates, although the elephant is well represented. The horse, as well as the ass, does not belch (K, II, 44). It has no gall (K, II, 184). Like the bull, it may continue to generate for some time after castration (K, III, 25); and it is very fond of water, whether for drinking or bathing (K, V, 258). The blood of the ass, like that of the elephant, is very thick and dark (K, VI, 149). The elephant differs from other animals in the articulation of its knees (K, VI, 77-78), but it has joints and does not need to sleep against trees (K, II, 179). Its testicles are contained within the body (K, VI, 78); its breasts are near, but not in, the pectoral region (K, V, 318). The tusks of the male are bent upward for battle; those of the female are straight or bent downward for support during pregnancy (K, V, 239, 317). Its gestation lasts two years (K, III, 195), and it swallows stones to cure indigestion (K, II, 270). Aristotle contradicts Ctesias at least twice about its seed (K, II, 57).

The references to members of the dog family are not numerous. Aristotle roughly proportions the time of blindness of whelps to the time of their gestation (K, II, 295); thus the blindness of whelps is not due to premature birth (K, II, 295). The stomach of the dog resembles that of man (K, V, 306). The hyena does not seem to be hermaphroditic (K, II, 249).

The few references to animals of the cat family are almost limited to sporadic details about their sexual processes. All retromingents copulate backward, as lions, hares (already mentioned), and lynxes (K, III, 134). No animal of the cat family smells sweet except the pard (K, III, 42).

Aristotle seems to have the bear cub born shapeless and licked into shape by the mother (K, II, 196).

Only two references are found to the aquatic Mammalia: the porpoise differs from the dolphin in having a dark-blue color and a broader back (K, VI, 141), and the dolphin's spout is on its back (K, V, 316).

As may be expected, the biological references to man are much more numerous and detailed than those to any other animal form. Man has no climacteric year (K, III, 62). Aristotle asserts warily that pygmies may exist (K, III, 50) and that they live near the headwaters of the Nile (K, III, 51). Only males are ambidextrous (K, III, 27), though all men should so become by practice (K, III, 27). Man alone does not become mad when bitten by a mad dog (K, V, 270). Aristotle asks why man coughs and oxen and cows do not (K, I, 173; K, II, 44). Sneezing indicates a healthy brain (K, III, 41). From noon to midnight sneezing is a sign of good luck; from midnight to noon it is unlucky (K, III, 41). Holding the breath cures hiccups (K, V, 227, 228). Fasting makes the breath smell (K, III, 47). A number of physiognomical references belong here. Man alone has grey hair (K, II, 44). A square forehead denotes a large soul (K, V, 5), whereas soft and effeminate persons are weak-kneed, have the head inclined to the right, are wavering in gait, and are furtive-eyed (K, V, 253). The picture and statue of Aristotle, says Browne, show him with his head inclined to the right, whereas Lysippus' picture of Alexander has his head inclined to the left, as befits a generous disposition (K, V, 290-291). Compassionate people are generators of women (K, V, 253). Aristotle says that people with double chins and varicose veins are less inclined than others to baldness (K, I, 188).

Anatomical references abound. Aristotle asks why the sun blackens men's skins, and why fire does not (K, III, 232-233). For his size, man has less distance between his eyes than any other animal (K, VI, 182), but the largest and dampest brain (K, VI, 146). He has the thinnest and purest of all blood (K, VI, 149). Like other Ancients, Aristotle includes in the thorax everything between the clavicles and the lower abdomen (K, V, 239; K, VI, 135). Aristotle wrongly thinks that men generally have no more than eight ribs on a side (K, III, 266), and that the stomach of man, much resembling that of a dog, is only a little larger than the intestine (K, V, 306), but there is something to be said for his statement that the heart is on the left side (K, III, 13). Some men have no gall, and they are long-lived (K, II, 211). Nothing but air enters the windpipe (K, VI, 146).

Perhaps because of his professional closeness to life processes, Browne shows a thoroughgoing interest in human reproduction, a fact which reminds us that many obstetrical books are listed in the sale catalogue of his library. Aristotle determines the fertility of human seed by whether it will sink in water (K, III, 32) or resist freezing (K, II, 89). Herodotus notwithstanding, the seed of Ethiopians is not black (K, III, 241-242). Aristotle suggests that man alone has pollutions in the night because he alone lies on his back (K, III, 9-10). The male becomes seminiferous at about fourteen (K, III, 224), but the female has no generative emission (K, II, 82-83; K, III, 309). The male organ, located at the base of the thorax (K, VI, 135), destroys the fertility of the seed if too long (K, III, 309). The story of Jupiter, Amphitryon, and Alcmaena affords an example of conception during pregnancy (K, II, 248). Gestation sometimes extends to eleven months (K, II, 53), and Egyptian children born during the eighth month manage to survive (K, III, 226). Children sometimes cry in the womb, but seldom at birth (K, V, 258). They sometimes cry but never weep and do not laugh when tickled until forty days after their birth (K, V, 258). White women have darker but less healthful milk than colored women; and milk high in casein is the most nourishing, but milk with less casein is more healthful (K, VI, 220-221). Unless Browne indexed to what he wanted, he must have read much more of Aristotle than appears in the above list to find among the commonplace materials these gems of information that interested him.

Other animal references are not associated with any particular form. Aristotle distinguishes the top and bottom, front and back, and right and left of animals according to the function of each part (K, III, 25-26). The right side predominates because it is customarily used more; however, the senses are equal on both sides because they are from the first in equal use (K, III, 22). There are three common parts to an animal: the mouth, the alimentary canal, and the anus (K, V, 328). Whether a monster is one or two animals depends on whether it has one or two hearts (K, II, 234-245). The nerves (K, II, 234-235) and the blood (K, VI, 149) originate in the heart.

Aristotle did not understand muscle (K, VI, 232-233). Portius has Aristotle saying that there is no fat about the heart or other hot parts of the body (K, VI, 90). All bones are connected together continuously (K, VI, 177). Aristotle frequently times astronomically the life functions of animals—by the rising of the Pleiades, or beginning of summer, and by the rising of the Dog Star, or the end of summer (K, III, 75)—though he uses some such qualifying words as "*Circa*" or "*magna ex parte*" (K, III, 223). Speaking of coagulation, Aristotle says, "γόνη σχίζεται" (K, V, 433). Aristotle conjectures that the testicles act as a counterweight to produce erection (K, III, 298). Hermaphrodites are potent in only one of the two sets of sexual organs (K, II, 246).

Browne seldom goes to Aristotle for knowledge of the vegetable kingdom. This is not surprising since not a single one of Aristotle's extant works is devoted to plants; however, a certain amount of material on plants is to be found in the animal books, especially *De generatione animalium*, and Browne unquestionably read the apocryphal *De plantis*. Aristotle's definition of sex precludes the notion that there is a mixed and undivided sex in plants (K, II, 161). The word "*Zizania*" does does not appear in Aristotle, and it is difficult to tell what species of plant it is (K, V, 53).

Most of the remaining factual references are also scientific, and many sciences are represented in these references: astronomy; chemistry; physics, especially meteorology; physiography; geology; mathematics; and psychology. Browne shows interest in nearly every branch of Aristotle's learning.

The astronomical references are not numerous. In a passage of ambiguous reference having to do with the transmission of light "beyond the tenth sphear," Browne is probably not referring to Aristotle's astronomy but to Aristotle's optics (K, I, 61; see page 87 *infra*). The allusion, "Whether Comets or blazing Stars be generally of such terrible effects, as elder times have conceived them" (K, III, 259), may be, as Wilkin says (quoting from Charles Blount's *Miscellaneous Works*, London, 1695, p. 63), to Aristotle's notion that comets are "accidental fires or meteors, kindled in the atmosphere" (W, III, 292, n. 9).

The references in chemistry and physics reflect Browne's widespread interest and extensive reading in the nature of matter. The passage, "Now the causes of liquation are contrary to those of concretion; and as the Atoms and indivisible parcels are united, so are they in an opposite way disjoyned" (K, II, 90), is based on Aristotle's *Meteorologica* ($382^{b}28$). There is a regular progressive transformation, says Aristotle, of "spirituous" material into water, and the water into earth—an obscure implication that bodies are first spirits (K, IV, 91). Unlike nutriment, air does not become progressively thicker under bodily heat (K, II, 261). Three kinds of smoke blacken bodies: the smoke from wood, bones, and hair; that from wax, resin, pitch, and turpentine; and that from oily bodies (K, III, 249). Aristotle distinguishes between soft fat, easily melting, and suety fat, not easily melting (K, VI, 90-91). He is mistaken in saying that salt more easily dissolves in cold water than in hot water (K, II, 44), in saying that a pot full of ashes will hold as much water as the same pot empty (K, II, 146), and probably in saying that arrows and bullets may be shot at such high velocity as to grow red hot or melt in flight (K, II, 151). He discredits the report that a man or beast cast bound into Lake Asphaltites will float as though swimming (K, III, 306). Hailstones falling from a great height become round and small; those falling a short distance remain irregular and large (K, II, 310). The nutcracker transmits forces by decussation (K, IV, 80-81). Since Browne kept well abreast of his century in his readings on matter and magnetism, subjects much advanced in his time by research, Aristotle is for Browne the physicist only one among many consulted. Aristotle warily calls the loadstone the stone that moves iron (K, II, 115). If Browne obtained little from Aristotle here, Aristotle could afford no more.

The number of references in meteorology and physiography is not large. A great winter abounding in rains and floods appears at regular intervals (K, VI, 350-351). A city open toward the east is more healthful than other cities because it receives earlier the rising sun, which dispels fog and dampness (K, III, 211). Browne lists for his son Edward fifteen statements about winds from *Problemata* (K, VI, 229). Egypt was built up out of the sea by deposits of the River Nile,[114] and the River Tanais (Don) will eventually deposit enough silt to make firm land of Maeotis Palus (Sea of Azov) (K, III, 216). Such gained ground loses its early fertility and later sinks to its former place (K, VI, 342). Since Aristotle seems not to have worked with tidal problems, the legend that he drowned himself in Euripus because he was frustrated at being unable to explain its tides is doubtful (K, III, 297-301). Aristotle has taken unnecessary pains to refute the physiography of Plato's myth about the conception of Tartarus, bottom of the place of torment (K, V, 206). Simplicius says that Callisthenes, at the request of Aristotle for information, found Babylonian records to extend back only 1,903 years or until ninety-five years after the flood (K, III, 162-163).

Apart from such mystical, astrological mathematics as we find in *The Garden of Cyrus*, Browne's interest in mathematics is slight, and to this slight thread Aristotle, not mathematically inclined himself, has been able to contribute only a strand or two. The decimal system, Aristotle observed, must have some foundation in nature since barbarians as well as Greeks use it (K, III, 54-55). And Aristotle seems to say that in Greece the vines of a vineyard are planted in quincuncial formation (K, IV, 74).

Several references relate in a broad sense to sensation. Aristotle was interested in a hollow roaring produced by air issuing from rocky apertures in marshes (K, II, 294). Taste is a kind of touch (K, II, 260). The story attributed to Aristotle that Philoxenus desired the neck of a crane for greater pleasure in gluttony is undoubtedly not true, as a reading elsewhere in Aristotle would imply (K, III, 303). Sight is produced by the passage of rays of light from the object to the eye (K, II, 202), but a medium is necessary for such passage (K, I, 61). In two definitions of beauty, Aristotle has made no mention of color (K, III, 246). He has written a tract on sleep but has not completely defined it (K, I, 93). He seems to doubt, quite unreasonably, says Brown, that there are divine dreams (K, V, 183).

Browne's interest in products of man's manufacture, seen

---

[114] K, III, 216; K, VI, 343, 349.

often in his correspondence with Edward, evokes a few references to Aristotle. Aristotle calls glass the "perfectest" work of art (K, III, 319). There is a certain "*humor mucrosus*" in the skin, possibly even in man's skin, from which glue may be made (K, V, 305). The Ancients made cheese with the sap of the fig tree as rennet (K, V, 362).

Browne's many-sided curiosity brings him to Aristotle for information on ancient customs. The custom of reclining at meals was observed in Aristotle's time (K, III, 101, 105). The single beds of Greece were more than six feet long and about three feet wide (K, IV, 84). Falconry had not progressed very far in ancient Greece since Aristotle shows little reliable knowledge of hawks and mentions only some crude practice of falconry in Thrace (K, V, 71, 75).

Browne could not find every fact he might want in Aristotle. Also, he could not use in *Pseudodoxia* all that he read and liked in *Historia animalium*. But, within the limits of what he could find and what he could use, his factual references reflect the nature and extent of his interest in the world of reality. His greatest interest is in animal biology, and his interest increases as he ascends the scale of animal forms. The hawk, the deer, cattle, and the elephant hold his attention for a considerable time; but his biology is homocentric, and he goes most often to Aristotle for facts about man, especially about human reproduction, a subject that he studies with some thoroughness and analogies to which have concerned him all the way up the *scala naturae*.[115] In fact, he applies Aristotle's and Scaliger's information about the male reproductive organs to every animal he can see or read about. He goes to bear gardens for observation on the subject, and even the royal emblem of England is not spared. Other facts of animal biology interest him, as the articulation of the joints that allows motion. What constitutes rightness and leftness, upness and downness in animals? What animals have no gall, and does its presence or absence affect the animal's economy of living? Dr. William Harvey's researches on the circulation of the blood send him to Aristotle for the

---

[115] Cf. Egon Stephen Merton, *Science and Imagination in Sir Thomas Browne* (New York, 1949), pp. 10-12.

consistency and color of the blood of various animals. How widespread in the animal kingdom are coughing, belching, and sneezing? How much credence is to be placed in physiognomy? Are those stories true that one hears about the beaver, the salamander, the basilisk, the pelican, the chameleon, and the bear? What causes the pigmentation of the skin? Why do monsters appear in nature—animals with abilities unknown to their kind, or with more or fewer than the regular number of bodily parts?

Other subjects engage less of his time—plant biology, astronomy, chemistry, physics, meteorology, physiography, mathematics, manufacturing processes, and ancient customs—but his real desire to know carries him into many bypaths and obscure corners of science. Some fields—politics, economics, and aesthetics—he barely touches or misses entirely, at least in his application to Aristotle's facts. He prefers the scientific, but he avoids even in human biology whatever is dull and ordinary. He skips pages on normal conception and gestation to pounce upon examples of superfetation and eleven-month pregnancies. For this reason, as well as the reasons that his medical practice occupied his time with the "importunity of uroscopy," that the method of *Pseudodoxia* focuses attention on the unusual, and that his age preferred the unusual, he is not a scholar in the modern sense but a dilettante who finds an extraordinarily wide range of things interesting.

BROWNE'S VIEW OF ARISTOTLE

Before turning to Browne's scholarship, we should consider the attitude with which he read Aristotle. In chapters 7 and 8 of the first book of *Pseudodoxia epidemica*, Browne discusses the evils of adherence to authority. His argument is that in many branches of learning we have gone beyond the Ancients, who were quite fallible and who tended to discourage original thought. Authority should always yield to reason and experiment, and it is valid only when they support it. Browne is committed to the negative side of ancient authority in *Pseudodoxia* by his program of dispelling old errors, but he does not prefer to be another René Descartes or Pierre Gassendi and to break with Aristotle, much less follow the example of Paracelsus, who, as Browne says, "hath reviled not onely the Authors, but almost all the learning that went before him" (K, II, 53). An attitude of intelligent acceptance of antiquity forms much of the working basis of *Pseudodoxia*. It is implicit in such statements as "we account it reasonable among our selves, and not injurious unto rational Authors, no farther to abet their Opinions then as they are supported by solid Reasons" (K, II, 52); and the same is expressed throughout Browne's works. He makes the Ancients not "the Judges of Truth" but "fellow Enquirers of it" (K, I, 124). He praises an author's points of strength and blames his weaknesses. Authority to him is one of the three "Determinators of Truth," along with reason and personal investigation (K, II, 195).

Browne ranks Aristotle as an authority below God and the churchmen, but he places him first among "human" authorities.[116] He regards him as one of the three great medical authorities,[117] but, as with other authorities, he examines his individual statements and practices to ascertain whether they are true or false. He finds Aristotle frequently evasive—sometimes to his credit, more often to his discredit—and not careful to verify his facts.[118] But, except for some outbursts of impatience, Browne is more than fair toward his authority. He is willing to strain the text a little to "salve" Aristotle,[119] and he remembers that the Stagirite is not at fault for the changes his contemporaries and successors have made in his texts and for the undue importance that ill-advised disciples have accorded him.[120]

---

[116] In listing authorities, Browne makes a practice of giving authorities that are "divine" first, then "human" authorities. Though appearing in lists with about thirty other "human" authorities, Aristotle stands more often at the head of a list than at any point in it; and he is cited or quoted much more often than any other author.

[117] Browne several times recommends Aristotle as a medical authority: K, VI, 65, 72-73, 84.

[118] K, II, 44, 115, 184, 196, 231; K, III, 50 (bis), 223, 224, 298; K, IV, 66.

[119] K, II, 186; K, III, 13, 26-27.

[120] K, II, 42-43; K, V, 206.

BROWNE AT WORK WITH CITATIONS AND QUOTATIONS

Nothing shows more significantly the quality of Browne's scholarship and his intellectual habits than his handling of citations and quotations. He refers to Aristotle in the works printed in the Keynes and the Wilkin editions altogether two hundred and ten times.[121] In these two hundred and ten references Browne mentions the various works of Aristotle seventy-eight times. This means that, in slightly fewer than two-thirds of the references, he makes no more definite indication of source than simply "Aristotle." This slight acknowledgment he manages to vary with great skill and dexterity in statement: "As Aristotle observeth" (K, VI, 77-78); "Aristotle sayth that" (K, VI, 141); "Aristotle with all his Philosophy hath not been able to prove" (K, I, 44); "not a negative from Aristotle" (K, I, 45); "according to Aristotle's Philosophy" (K, I, 61); and so on. Browne seldom repeats in full any one formula for inserting the reference. He uses all the words of asseveration, sometimes in the active, sometimes in the passive, with variations in word order and construction. Aristotle's attitude toward his material, his method of statement, and Browne's opinion of his material also supply a variety of leads.

Of the seventy-eight references in Browne to the works of Aristotle, fifty-four consist of no more than the name of Aristotle and the name of the work. There is great variety in the manner of reference. Sometimes the mention of the title is very unobtrusive: "What Aristotle alledgeth in that Problem; why" (K, III, 10); "the Political advice of Aristotle" [for the advice of Aristotle in *Politica*] (K, III, 27); and "those physionomicall notes of Aristotle" [reference to the apocryphal *Physiognomonica*] (K, V, 253). Other references to titles are more direct, but none the less varied in style: "Aristotle, who w[r]itt *De motu aut incessu animalium*" (K, VI, 232); "Aristotle, as he delivereth in his Book, *De incessu Animalium*" (K,

---

[121] This figure does not include every mention of the name "Aristotle" and the personal pronoun "he" referable to him. A reference is counted as one if it involves one set of materials in Aristotle's works or one idea about him. All the references to him as a man in the chapter "Of the Death of Aristotle" (*Pseudodoxia*, Bk. VII, chap. 13; K, III, 297-302) are counted as one.

II, 179); "Aristotle, who hath written a singular Tract *Of Sleep*" (K, I, 93); and others. But nothing matches the variety of references to *Historia animalium*. Translators never could agree upon a Latin title, and Browne exercises his prerogative to the full: "Aristotle in his *History of Animals* is";[122] "*Aristotle, lib. animal.*" (K, V, 258); "from Aristotle *de Animal.*";[123] "upon Aristot. *de Animalibus*" (K, VI, 135); and "*in Arist. de historia animalium*" (K, VI, 210). This by no means completes the list.

Of the twenty-four more detailed references that remain, seventeen give only the book of the work in which the reference is found.[124] If the reference is in the text of a work intended for general publication, it is always cryptic and fused into the structure of the sentence: "that [error] in the fourth of his Meteors" (K, II, 44); "Aristotle is so indistinct in their names and numbers, that in the first of *Meteors* he" (K, III, 216); "and Aristotle himself in the eighth of his *Politicks*, speaks" (K, III, 303). Browne shows less versatility of reference as the complexity of reference grows. In the footnotes and margins of works intended for publication and in the text of Letters and Commonplace Books, he states the reference more plainly: "Problem Sec. 33 [marginal note in *Pseudodoxia*]" (K, III, 41); "Aristot. *Hist. Animal. lib.* 8 [marginal note in *Certain Miscellany Tracts*, Tract 1]" (K, V, 50); "as Aristotle delivers & Scaliger not directly rejecteth, *lib.* 8, *hist. Animal.* [Commonplace Books]" (K, V, 258); and "Aristotle *de histor. anim., lib.* 1. [Letters]" (K, VI, 146).

Only seven references of the two hundred and ten may lay claim to scholarly documentation in the modern acceptation of the term: "See Aristotle's *Ethicks*, chapter of Magnanimity [marginal note in *Christian Morals*]" (K, I, 107); "ARISTOT. DE HISTORIA ANIMALIUM LIB. 2, CAP. 1. VERSIONIS SCALIGERIANAE [rubric to passage in the paper "De Astragalo aut Talo"]" (W, IV, 298); "*Aristot. lib.* 8. *cap.* 22 *de hist. Animalium.* [Commonplace Books]" (K, V, 270); "in the same place pag 95 [Letters,

---

[122] K, II, 187; also, with slight variations, K, V, 306, 316.
[123] K, V, 362; K, VI, 65.
[124] One of the seventeen is of doubtful classification: " ... we shall instance only in three of his Problems, and all contained under one Section" (K, II, 44).

reference to *Historia animalium*, Scaliger edition]" (K, VI, 135); "*Aristotelis lib. 2 historia Animal. cap. 5.* [Commonplace Books]" (K, V, 239); "Aristot. in historia animal, lib. 3 cum Comment. Julii Scaligeri pag. 372. [Letters]" (K, VI, 149); "*Aristot. hist. animalium, lib. 1.* [in text of Letters]" and "*lib. i. cap. cliiii.*[125] [in margin at same point]" (K, VI, 182).

A desire to keep his style mellifluous and rhythmic probably accounts at least in part for Browne's failure to give more definite references. Citation of work, chapter, page, and line would spoil the cadence of some of the famous passages in *Religio medici* and *Urn Burial*. It is significant that works intended for the general public, as *Religio medici, Pseudodoxia epidemica, Urn Burial,* and *The Garden of Cyrus*, have a much higher proportion of indefinite source references than the Letters, intended for the eyes of son Edward alone.[126] Almost all references giving more than just the particular work of Aristotle are in these three parts of Browne's works in descending order of numerousness: (1) the Letters, (2) the Commonplace Books, and (3) footnotes and marginal notes of works intended for the general public. There are instances in which definite references in the early editions of *Pseudodoxia* have been relegated to the margin or foot of the page in later editions.[127]

Of the two hundred and ten references to Aristotle in the works of Browne, one hundred and fifty-four, or about five-sevenths, are citations without quotation. The quotations in the fifty-six remaining references are in Greek, Latin, and English. Greek appears in twenty-nine references; Latin in forty-six; and English in eight. Browne quotes Greek alone seven times; Latin, twenty-four times; and English, once. Combinations of

---

[125] This number seems to be wrong. In *The Works of Aristotle Translated into English*, ed. J. A. Smith and W. D. Ross, 12 vols. (Oxford, 1908-52), vol. IV (1910), trans. by D'Arcy Wentworth Thompson, it is chap. 15; Scaliger's edition: *Aristotelis Historia de animalibus; Iulio Caesare Scaligero interprete cum eiusdem commentarijs* (Toulouse, 1619), chap. 16.

[126] H. F. Fletcher, *The Use of the Bible in Milton's Prose*, Univ. of Ill. Stud. in Lang. and Lit., XIV, No. 3 (Aug. 1929), 20, observes the same practice in Milton's use of biblical references.

[127] As in Bk. II, chap. 6 (passage corresponding to one in K, II, 161). This matter has been treated fully in the unpublished thesis of Tipton Marshall Westfall, "Sir Thomas Browne's Revisions in *Pseudodoxia Epidemica*: A Study in the Development of His Mind" (Princeton, 1939).

all three languages appear three times; Greek and Latin, seventeen times; Latin and English, twice; and Greek and English, twice.

The quotations range from single words, all but submerged in their context, to complete sentences. The Greek is written in Greek characters in all but two quotations. Referring to a certain grape beetle described by Aristotle, which is deadly to cattle, Browne uses the word *Staphilimus* (K, II, 299). The word in the Greek is σταφυλῖνος; and the Latin in Scaliger's translation of *Historia animalium*[128] and elsewhere is *pastinaca*. Browne has transliterated, changing υ to *i* and ος to *us*, following standard practice. In *Religio medici* he writes ἐντελέχεια (W, II, 15), but transliterates in "Of the Answers of the Oracle of Apollo at Delphos to Croesus King of Lydia" (in *Certain Miscellany Tracts*) to the Latin form *Entelecheia* (K, V, 120).

Eighteen of Browne's twenty-nine Greek quotations agree with a Greek text in Browne's possession or, when his text is not known, with a modern text of Aristotle.[129] Of the forty-six Latin quotations, only eight agree with known texts, and only nine of the remainder agree sufficiently in content with standard texts and translations of Aristotle to offer any real possibility that they could agree with texts as yet unknown. The rest of the quotations, Greek and Latin, Browne has altered in ways that we shall presently consider. The eight English quotations are all clearly Browne's translations from the Greek or Latin. There is no evidence that Browne had any English translations of Aristotle.

Browne went for his final authority on Aristotle's dicta to the original, the Greek, text, as the context of the quotations often indicates. As the data in the above paragraph indicate, he did not feel so much at liberty to alter the Greek text as the Latin translations, which were more frequently used than the Greek because he could work more easily with the Latin and because the Latin was more intelligible to most readers. We see

---

[128] P. 971; *Historia animalium*, 604b18. The Greek texts quoted in this study are as they appear in the Keynes edition or, when not available in that edition, in the Wilkin edition.

[129] Aside from accentuation, differences between the Greek texts of Aristotle available in Browne's time and modern texts are slight.

him quoting the Greek and Latin together, the Greek first for authority and the Latin, and possibly also English, for the convenience of the reader. There is nothing, however, so sacred about the Greek text that Browne cannot disregard it on occasion. Once Scaliger does not translate accurately, and in another place he omits in translation, both times with Browne's approval.[130]

Sometimes Browne gives an alternative spelling to the one in the Greek or Latin text. He substitutes δύσπληκτον for δυσέκπληκτον (K, VI, 25). Both are correct spellings, but Browne has altered the word to make it less emphatic—"cannot be struck with terror" instead of "cannot be completely struck with terror." He substitutes the alternative spellings μεξων for μείξων (K, V, 306), and *fetidus* for *foetidus* (K, VI, 229). Such changes are minor.

He frequently trims away unnecessary parts of quotations, even if it is necessary to reshape what remains. A passage in *De anima* (405ª20) is λίθον ἔφη ψυχὴν ἔχειν, ὅτι τὸν σίδηρον κινεῖ, which may be translated, "He said stone has a soul because it moves the iron." Since he is at the moment interested in magnetism, Browne cuts out the irrelevant material about the soul, ἔφη ψυχὴν ἔχειν, changes the accusative of discourse λίθον to the nominative, and changes ὅτι ("because") to ὅστις ("which"). The result is λίθος ὅστις τὸν σίδηρον κινεῖ, which he follows with an accurate Latin translation: *"Lapis qui ferrum movet"* (K, II, 115). He does much the same with Latin quotations. In a letter to Edward he quotes a passage on bones that he has found in this form in Scaliger's translation of *Historia animalium*: "Ossa cum ab uno dependent omnia; tum inter se sunt continuata, quemadmodum et venae segregatum os nullum invenies" (516ª8). In reshaping, Browne sharpens his focus by dropping the idea that all bones are connected to one bone. He also drops the "cum...tum" construction to reduce the three clauses to a simplified two: " ... *ossa inter se sunt continuata quemadmodum et venae segregatum os nullum invenies*" (K, VI, 177). He often drops words, phrases, and whole clauses to eliminate unneces-

---

[130] K, III, 223, 50.

77

sary connectives and the irrelevant, as well as to shorten and to simplify.[131]

For various reasons Browne changes the phraseology of many of his quotations. In Scaliger's translation and edition of *Historia animalium* appears this passage, τίκτει δὲ μικρὰ ἐχίδια ἐν ὑμέσιν, οἱ περιρρήγνυνται τριταῖοι, ἐνίοτε δὲ καὶ ἔσωθεν διαφαγόντα αὐτὰ ἐξέρχεται (558ᵃ29), having to do with the birth of vipers. In Browne's quotation of this passage (K, II, 241), Scaliger's third person plural present indicative passive περιρρήγνυνται becomes the corrupt form περιήγνωνται, which may have been intended as the third person plural perfect indicative passive περιήγνυνται of a different verb. In their infinitive form, both verbs mean "to break all around." Browne has made other changes as well: δὲ, a weak connective, is omitted; ἐχίδνα, the more regular form of ἐχίδια is used; and οἱ, masculine to agree with ὑμέσιν, is changed by mistake to αἱ, the feminine.

Comparison of the two passages set down below shows a drastic change in phraseology and content. The first is from Scaliger's translation of *Historia animalium* (499ᵇ27), and the second is Browne's version of the same passage (W, IV, 298).

Ut superior pars extrorsum, inferior autem introrsum spectet. Et quae Coa dicuntur, intus inter se obversa: quae appellantur Chia, foris: quae antennae nominantur, superne.

Quod est pronum, foris; quod est supinum, introrsum spectat: ita ut quae Coa et felicia dicuntur, intus inter se obversa; quae Chia et infelicia, foris; quae Antennae sive cornua dicuntur, superne.

At first sight these two passages seem to represent entirely different versions; however, Browne labels his passage "Versionis Scaligerianae." He has converted the result clause in present subjunctive, which begins Scaliger's version, to two noun clauses used as alternative subjects of an independent clause in present indicative. In this way he has divorced the Scaliger version from grammatical dependence upon material he is not quoting.

---

[131] For other examples, compare the Greek of K, V, 258 with *Historia animalium*, 605ᵃ12; of K, VI, 146 with *Historia animalium*, 494ᵇ28. Compare the Latin of K, II, 207 and 249 with Scaliger's translation of *Historia animalium*, 578ᵇ23 and 579ᵇ16, respectively; of K, V, 227 with Ludovicus Septalius, *Ludovici Septalii ... in Aristotelis Problemata commentaria, ab eo Latinè facta....*, 3 vols. (Lyons, 1632), 962ᵃ1.

Scaliger's *superior pars extrorsum* and *inferior autem introrsum* are not clear, carrying an apparent contradiction in terms. Browne's *quod est pronum, foris* and *quod est supinum, introrsum*, while not completely clear, have at least the virtue of internal consistency. In the rest of the passage, Browne makes a cento of Aristotle's description (in Scaliger's Latin) of the hucklebones of animals and of materials of his own about the dice that were made in ancient times from these hucklebones. Aristotle's mention of the gambling terms "Coa" (the lucky sides with the size points) and "Chia" (the unlucky sides with the ace points), gave Browne his cue. Other changes: *et quae* becomes *ita ut quae*, which gives a stronger effect of unity of thought; *appellantur* and *nominantur* give way for economy to a single *dicuntur*, although the word has already been used above; and *sive cornua* is added to clarify *antennae*.[132]

Sometimes, though in no consistent fashion, Browne changes his quoted Greek or Latin text to adapt it to its new context. Speaking of the eyes of the mole, Browne says, "Aristotle terms them πηρουμένους, which Gaza translates *Oblaesos*, and Scaliger by a word of imperfection *inchoatos*" (K, II, 251). In Scaliger's translation and edition of *Historia animalium*, the Greek is πηρουμένων and the Latin is *inchoatos* (491ᵇ34). The word in Gaza is *oblesique*.[133] Scaliger's *inchoatos* proves to be the controlling factor. Either because the English context calls for accusative plural masculine or because Browne saw *inchoatos* first, he has made the Greek and Gaza's Latin conform to it. Πηρουμένων, genitive plural, becomes the accusative πηρουμένους; the suffix "que" is dropped from *oblesique*, the spelling is altered slightly, and the form becomes accusative plural masculine. In

---

132 For another change in Greek phrasing, compare W, IV, 298 and Scaliger's translation of *Historia animalium*, 499ᵇ29. For other changes in Latin phrasing, compare K, V, 258 and Scaliger's commentary to *Historia*, p. 845; K, V, 305 and Scaliger's *Historia*, 517ᵇ28; K, VI, 177 and Scaliger's commentary to *Historia*, p. 325; K, VI, 221 and Scaliger's *Historia*, 522ᵇ18; K, II, 241 and Scaliger's *Historia*, 558ᵃ31. In a letter to Edward, June 20, 1679 (K, VI, 135), and another, February 14, 1680-1 (K, VI, 210), Browne quotes the same passage from Scaliger's commentary to *Historia* (p. 96). In each instance, he alters the phrasing and in a different fashion.

133 The Gaza edition used here is *Aristotelis De natura animalium....De partibus animalium....De generatione animalium.... Theodoro Gaza interprete* (Venice, 1513).

this instance Browne has ironed out nonconformity in his Greek and Latin quotations, but this is by no means his invariable rule in quotations, as the following example shows. Of the external ear, there is "the superior part called by Aristotle ἀνώνυμον or *innominata*" (K, V, 300). The Greek adjective, meaning "anonymous," is nominative singular neuter, as it is in Scaliger's text (*Historia*, 492ª15), and Browne follows his own frequent practice of keeping or adopting the nominative in quotations, but his Latin translation is nominative singular feminine and, so, does not match in gender. Elsewhere Browne is more careful. In his reference to the cinnamon bird, he says it is "called . . . by Aristotle, *Cinnamomus*" (K, II, 220). Here he adopts the nominative though Scaliger uses the accusative after "vocant" (*Historia*, 616ª7). In another reference, this time in a marginal note, Browne, for no apparent reason, keeps the accusative plural of the original, ἀμπέλων συστάδας,[134] though reversing the order of these two words to make them conform to English word order. The English word order determines the order of the Greek in a quotation about sneezing: "And therefore saith Aristotle, they that hear it, προσκυνοῦσιν ὡς ἵερον, honor it as somewhat sacred" (K, III, 41). Browne has moved προσκυνοῦσιν from the end of the quotation (*Problemata*, 962ª35) to the beginning to make the word order in the Greek quotation the same as in his English translation that follows it.

We have already seen[135] how Browne reshapes the Scaliger passage containing the gambling terms "Coa" and "Chia" to make it intelligible in its new context. Another example is his reshaping of a passage about the coagulation of blood. The passage in Scaliger is "Foris autem concrescit omnium, praeterquam cervi, et damae, et si quid eiusdem naturae est" (*Historia*, 520ᵇ23). Besides dropping the transitional *autem*, as he does so often, and the unnecessary *et damae*, changing the spelling of *praeterquam*, mistaking *natura* for *naturae*, Browne has changed the passage to make it intelligible outside its context in Scaliger's translation and in a different context. *Extra venas* is substituted for the vague *foris*, and *sanguis* is inserted to take the place of

---

134 K, IV, 74, n.; *Politica*, 1330ᵇ29.
135 See p. 78-79 *supra*.

"it" as the subject of the verb *concrescit* and of the sentence. The result is: "*extra venas concrescit omnium sanguis preterquam cervi, et si quid ejusdem natura est*" (K, VI, 175).

In one instance Browne rejects the Latin translation of a Greek word given in the Aristotle text in favor of a translation suggested immediately below in the commentary. Scaliger translates the word πυγηδόν in his *Historia* as *clunibus* but gives this listing in the commentary: "πυγηδόν, *clunatim*. Theodorus, *aversa*."[136] Perhaps the handy juxtaposition of Greek and Latin in the commentary led to Browne's choice: πυγηδόν, *clunatim*, or aversly, as Lions, Hares, Linxes" (K, III, 134). Even the *aversa* of Theodore Gaza works its way into Browne's version of Aristotle's text as "aversly."

As some of the examples given above have illustrated, Browne is prone to errors in transcription. A few other examples will illustrate the point. Εγκέφαλον in Scaliger's Greek text (*Historia*, 494b28) becomes ἐνκέφαλον in Browne (K, VI, 146)—an easy mistake to make since ν and γ sound much alike before κ. In a letter to Edward, Browne quotes Scaliger's commentary on the deer. "Os in corde habere cervam, et cervam in *valva* nos expert sumus [my italics]" (K, VI, 175). The passage in Scaliger's commentary is actually: "Os in corde habere et cervam in *vulva*, et nos experti sumus [my italics]" (*Historia*, p. 254). With his mind on the heart of the deer, Browne has mistaken a *u* for an *a* and so changed radically the location of the bone. The loss of *i* from *experti* is another mistake in transcription.

Nowhere does Browne show greater love of experimenting with texts and translations than in his work with *Problemata*. The Latin passages that make up the body of "Notae in Aristotelem" are from Septalius (cited in note 131 *supra*), but very freely changed (W, IV, 361-366). Other passages show that, if he had the Latin of *Problemata* before him, he also had the Greek.[137] The paper that he "formerly writt out of Aristoteles, problemes of winds" (K, VI, 228-229) shows substantial agreement with Septalius' text. Here too Browne has telescoped and

---

136 Text, 539b22; commentary, p. 520.
137 As K, III, 41; K, V, 227.

improved the text, changing the interrogative characteristic of *Problemata* into the affirmative.

The Greek text is Browne's ultimate authority, but he does not make practical resort to its evidence as frequently or as insistently as Milton turned to the Hebrew and Greek. We have already seen instances in which he has altered the Greek text and then made his own translations in Latin or English of the altered text; but, with the unaltered Greek text before him, he prefers to rely on the translations of others. There are only two clear-cut instances in which, without altering the Greek text, he has given his own version precedence over the versions of others, and in both of these instances the Greek itself has given the translators such difficulty as to produce widely varying translations. In the first instance, Pliny, Scaliger, and Gaza are, as Browne says, at odds:

... Τίκτει δὲ ἐν μιᾷ ἡμέρᾳ καθ' ἕν, τίκτει δὲ πλείω ἢ εἴκοσιν, which are literally thus translated, *Parit autem una die secundum unum, parit autem plures quam viginti*, and thus may be Englished, She bringeth forth in one day one by one, and sometimes more than twenty ... (K, II, 241.)

The second instance concerns the Pygmies:

The first [testimony] of Aristotle, whose words are these, ἐστὶ δὲ ὁ τόπος, &c. That is, *Hic locus est quem incolunt Pygmaei, non enim id fabula est, sed pusillum genus ut aiunt*. Wherein indeed Aristotle plaies the Aristotle, that is, the wary and evading assertor; For though with *non est fabula*, he seems at first to confirm it, yet at the last he claps in, *Sicut aiunt*, and shakes the belief he put before upon it. And therefore I observe Scaliger hath not translated the first ... (K, III, 50.)

Scaliger translates the appropriate passage in Aristotle:

Ea loca sunt quae Pygmaei incolunt: pusillum genus, ut aiunt. (*Historia*, 597a6.)

In Gaza's translation the passage is:

... quo in loco pugnare cum pigmaeis dicunt, non enim id fabula est, sed certe genus tum horum, tum et equorum pusillum (ut dicit) est.

Two Greek manuscript traditions clash at this point. One is represented in the first clause of Scaliger's translation, the other in the first clause of Gaza's. It is apparent that Browne follows the tradition represented in Scaliger's translation according to which the Pygmies *dwell* instead of *being fought with*. To make his translation, Browne consults both Scaliger and Gaza. *Pusillum genus ut aiunt* is supplied by Scaliger. But Browne has consulted the Greek text and, in doing so, has discovered the part Scaliger has scorned to translate. This part Gaza supplies: *non enim id fabula est*. However, the break with the translators comes at the very beginning: ἐστὶ δὲ ὁ τόπος. Obviously the noun is singular and Scaliger's *Ea loca sunt* must be wrong. Browne's translation is, then, *Hic locus est*.

Sometimes Browne's translations from the Greek are fairly literal, as in his treatment of Aristotle's remark about sneezing: "they that hear it, προσκυνοῦσιν ὡς ἱερον, honour it as somewhat sacred" (K, III, 41). But he can also translate freely, as in a passage on the eyes of moles: "we discerned no more then Aristotle mentions, τῶν ὀφθαλμῶν μέλαινα, that is, a black humour" (K, II, 251).[138] Here Browne's free translation makes Aristotle somewhat more definite about what he sees than he is in the Greek.

It is clear from much that has gone before that Browne is by no means careful to deal fairly and accurately with Aristotle. The errors and types of errors are so numerous as to deserve special attention.

In eight instances material is attributed to the Stagirite that is not to be found in him at all. Two of these have to do with the same story, "that a Bever to escape the Hunter, bites off his testicles," and Browne locates the story more definitely in Aristotle than usual, in the "Ethicks" (K, II, 66, 190). In another instance Aristotle is credited with the supposed fact that the buzzard has three testicles (K, II, 234). Whether or not by coincidence, both accounts may be located in Pliny.[139] A statement concerning the unequal leg lengths in frogs, locusts, grasshoppers, beetles, and spiders is assigned by Browne to Aristotle's *De incessu animalium* (K, II, 195), but it is not to be located either here or elsewhere in Aristotle. A statement that children have been heard to cry in the womb is assigned to

---

138 Literally, "black of the eyes."
139 *Natural History*, trans. J. Bostock and H. T. Riley (London, 1855-57), Bk. XXXII, chap. 13; Bk. XXXVII, chap. 21; Bk. X, chap. 9.

Historia animalium (K, V, 258), but only related material
appears in Aristotle.[140] The three remaining statements—that
glass is the "perfectest" work of art (K, III, 319), that the variegation of birds is from their living in the sun (K, III, 298), and
that spiders cast off their skin "often in the year" (K, VI, 80)
—are assigned simply to Aristotle. Only one of the three, the
last, has any counterpart in Aristotle, and this only by giving
a curious twist to the meaning.[141] Of these eight statements
that are not to be located in Aristotle, the source in four instances is given more definitely than is usual with Browne. The
only possible explanation for these eight errors is Browne's
having cited from memory and been mistaken about either the
material or the source. Most of these errors, like most of the
references to Aristotle in general, are in *Pseudodoxia epidemica*.
The others are in the Commonplace Books and the Letters.

Browne's citation of definite sources is not always to be
trusted, as examples given above and other examples show. He
gives "Meteors" as the source of the idea that arrows and bullets
may be discharged with such force as to melt in flight (K, II,
151). Though *Meteorologica* would seem the logical source, the
actual source is *De caelo* (289ª21). Here is another error of
the same kind: In the 1646 and 1650 editions of *Pseudodoxia*,
Browne speaks of bellowings produced by forcing air through
narrow apertures, "which," he says, "Aristotle abserveth in a
problem of the 25. section." This is the correct source.[142] But,
when the style was enhanced by moving the source outside the
text in editions after 1650, the "25" was changed by mistake
to "XV" and Browne was not sufficiently alert as a proofreader
to catch the mistake.

In several references Browne is correct as far as he goes, but
he has not read widely enough in Aristotle to discover his mis-
understanding. In this reference, Browne's modest statement,
taken by itself, is completely correct: "Aristotle, I confess, in
his acute and singular Book of *Physiognomy*, hath made no
mention of Chiromancy" (K, I, 75). Browne's statement con-

---

[140] *Historia animalium*, 587ª33.
[141] *Historia animalium*, 623ª30.
[142] *Problemata*, Bk. XXV, chap. 2 (937ᵇ38); see K, II, 294.

fines the inquiry to *Physiognomonica*, but its context carries the implication that Aristotle had no knowledge of chiromancy. On the contrary, he speaks of it, not in *Physiognomonica*, but elsewhere,[143] and he is often credited with originating it.

In another instance Browne apparently has not noted or followed Aristotle's suggestion that more material on a subject is available further on. The discussion in *Religio medici* has turned to dreams: "Aristotle, who hath written a singular Tract *Of Sleep*, hath not, methinks, th[o]roughly defined it; . . . for those *Noctambuloes* and nightwalkers, though in their sleep, do yet injoy the action of their senses" (K, I, 93). In the first chapter of *De somno et vigilia* (453ᵇ25), Aristotle defines sleep as the opposite of waking, waking being the state in which sense perception takes place. Thus far Browne is right; then in chapter 2 Aristotle makes a promise that covers Browne's objection, "Some persons move in their sleep, and perform many acts like waking acts, but not without a phantasm or an exercise of sense-perception; for a dream is in a certain way a sense-impression. But of them we have to speak later on" (456ᵃ26). Accordingly, at the end of *De somniis* (462ᵃ27), the treatise on dreams, Aristotle speaks of sense perception during sleep and reaches this conclusion, "For it is quite possible that, of waking or sleeping, while the one [waking] is present in the ordinary sense, the other [sleeping] also should be present in a certain way." Aristotle has met Browne's objection: to the extent that "*Noctambuloes*" "injoy the action of their senses," they are awake. Quite likely Browne read as far as the end of chapter 2 of *De somno et vigilia*, far enough to note and make capital of the apparent inconsistency that Aristotle points out in his own definition, and no farther.

The next example illustrating Browne's incomplete reading in Aristotle also concerns definition:

For though Empedocles affirm, there is a mixt, and undivided Sex in Vegetables; and Scaliger upon Aristotle, doth favourably explain that opinion; yet will it not consist with the common and ordinary acception, nor yet with Aristotle's definition. For if that be Male which generates in another, that Female which procreates in it self; if it be understood of

---

[143] *Historia animalium*, 493ᵇ32; *Problemata*, 896ᵃ37, 964ᵃ33.

Sexes conjoined, all Plants are Female; and if of disjoined and congressive generation, there is no Male or Female in them at all. (K, II, 161.)

A footnote by Browne sends us to *De plantis*. There we find, as Browne says, the opinion of Empedocles that the sexes are mixed in plants and the opposing opinion of "Aristotle" that plants do not meet the requirement of sex that it be differentiated in individuals (816^{b}40). But Aristotle did not write *De plantis*; and the point of view in *De plantis* differs widely from Aristotle's. One passage from many in *De generatione animalium* will serve: "For to the essence of plants belongs no other function or business than the production of seed; since, then, this is brought about by the union of male and female, Nature has mixed these and set them together in plants, so that the sexes are not divided in them" (731^{a}24). In other words, Aristotle holds the view that Browne and *De plantis* ascribe to Empedocles, a view directly opposite to that of the author of *De plantis*. Browne either has not read the passages in *De generatione* or is unaware of them for the moment. Since, however, he was not aware that *De plantis* is apocryphal, he could not be on his guard against it.

Three of the five or six examples of insufficient reading occur in Browne's first work, *Religio medici*, which he wrote at the age of about thirty.[144] Other types of error are abundant throughout the later works, but this fault has been largely corrected.

Sometimes Browne labels material "Aristotle" in such a careless way as to raise doubts about just what and how much the name covers and where the material is to be found. Sometimes this ambiguity is stylistic in origin. Here is parallelism of sentence structure but not of thought: "There is no Attribute that adds more difficulty to the mystery of the Trinity, where, though in a relative way of Father and Son, we must deny a priority. I wonder how Aristotle could conceive the World eternal, or how he could make good two Eternities" (K, I, 16).

---

[144] For other examples, compare K, I, 95 and *Ethica Nicomachea*, 1120^{b}7; K, II, 227 and *Historia animalium*, 541^{a}3. In his foreword to *Religio medici*, Browne explains at least in part his insufficient reading for that work: "It was penned in such a place,...that...I had not the assistance of any good Book whereby to ... relieve my memory" (K, I, 4).

Aristotle does "conceive the World eternal," but he never tries to "make good two Eternities"; in fact, he denies such a possibility.[145] The best interpretation here is that Browne is not really saying that Aristotle tries to "make good two Eternities." Aristotle would have to validate two eternities if he tried to reconcile his imperfect philosophy with the perfect truth of religion, in which there are a Father and a Son who have between them two eternities. The "how or how" construction tricks the reader into expecting parallelism of thought, whereas there is complete divergence.

In the following passage, the words "according to Aristotle's Philosophy" could be applied to either of two statements: "I grant that two bodies placed beyond the tenth sphear, or in a vacuity, according to Aristotle's Philosophy, could not behold each other, because there wants a body or Medium to hand and transport the visible rays of the object unto the sense" (K, I, 61). The first statement, that two bodies placed beyond the tenth sphere are in a void, is contrary to Aristotle's philosophy since he denies the existence of a void.[146] The second, that two bodies cannot behold each other in a void because of the lack of a medium, strikes a better balance with Aristotle's philosophy;[147] and, since it is closer to the central theme of the passage, it is probably the interpretation meant. Such confusion as this is quite likely due to the confused state of the commonplace books in which Browne jotted down without careful system stores of materials that he later used in writing.

In the next passage the problem lies in determining what "which conceit" refers to:

The first shall be of the Elephant, whereof there generally passeth an opinion it hath no joints; and this absurdity is seconded with another, that being unable to lie down, it sleepeth against a Tree; which the Hunters observing, do saw it almost asunder; whereon the Beast relying, by the fall of the Tree, falls also down it self, and is able to rise no more. *Which conceit* [my italics] is not the daughter of later times, but an old and gray-headed error, even in the days of Aristotle, as he delivereth in his Book, *De incessu animalium,* . . . (K, II, 179.)

---

[145] *De caelo,* Bk. I, chap. 12.
[146] *Physica,* 214ᵇ12—217ᵇ29; *De caelo,* 279ᵃ12-13, 287ᵃ11-14.
[147] *De anima,* 419ᵃ12, 434ᵇ27; *De sensu et sensibili,* 440ᵃ17.

We should normally expect "Which conceit" to refer to the material on the hunting of elephants immediately preceding; however, this material is not Aristotle's but Scaliger's and Browne's.[148] For the antecedent of "Which conceit," we must go all the way back to the clause: "it [the elephant] hath no joints."[149]

In the following passage Browne attacks the vulgar error "that Jews stink" by examining their diet:

Of Fishes they [Jews] only tast of such as have both fins and scales; which are comparatively but few in number, such only, saith Aristotle, whose Egg or spawn is arenaceous; whereby are excluded all cetacious and cartilagineous Fishes; many pectinal, whose ribs are rectilineal; many costal, which have their ribs embowed; all spinal, or such as have no ribs, but only a back bone, or somewhat analogous thereto, as Eels, Congers, Lampries; all that are testaceous, as Oysters, Cocles, Wilks, Scollops, Muscles; and likewise all crustaceous, as Crabs, Shrimps and Lobsters. (K, III, 45.)

Aristotle would seem to be a commanding presence in this account. To begin with, however, he never anywhere mentions the Jews; his only certain contribution is the fact that scaly fishes lay eggs with hard integuments—"arenaceous" eggs.[150] The fins are necessary to the Jewish dietary law but have nothing to do with Aristotle. With two parts Jewish dietary law ("Jews" and "fins and scales") and one part Aristotle ("arenaceous" eggs), Browne sets up three qualifications— fins, scales, "arenaceous" eggs—and, perhaps occasionally resorting to Aristotle for type definitions, he eliminates six classes of fishes. Aristotle's role is less imposing than the loose reference to him would imply.

The instances in which the name of Aristotle covers too much territory are matched by instances in which it should cover more of the context than appears from Browne's acknowledgment. Here Aristotle's contextual phraseology is taken:

---

[148] Scaliger's contribution, in his commentary to *Historia animalium* (p. 153), is the statement that the elephant sleeps against a tree.
[149] *De incessu animalium*, 709ª9; *Historia animalium*, 498ª8.
[150] *De generatione animalium*, 733ª17, 733ᵇ7.

... that merry one [example of superfetation] in Plautus urged also by Aristotle: that is, of Iphicles and Hercules, the one begat by Jupiter, the other by Amphitryon upon Alcmaena; as also in those super-conceptions, where one child was like the father, the other like the adulterer, the one favoured the servant, the other resembled the master. (K, II, 148.)

Actually the debt to Aristotle does not stop at the Amphitryon story, but continues through the phraseology about the husband and the adulterer.[151] In the same way Aristotle silently furnishes an uncut gem for this rightly admired bit of prose:

... and if according to the *Elogy* of Solon, a man may be only said to be happy after he is dead, and ceaseth to be in the visible capacity of beatitude, or if according unto his own *Ethicks* [Aristotle's], sense is not essential unto felicity, but a man may be happy without the apprehension thereof; surely in that sense he is pyramidally happy ... (K, III, 302.)

Not only the lack of connection between "sense" and "felicity," but Solon's opinion about happiness after death comes in one piece from *Ethica Nicomachea* (1100^a10).[152]

Sometimes Browne roughly lumps together Aristotle and other sources without any indication that their contributions are unequal. Aristotle, Alhazen (Abu-'Ali Al-Hasan Ibn Al-Haytham), and Vitello (or Vitellio or Witelo) are cited to prove there is no basilisk.

But lastly, That this destruction should be the effect of the first beholder, or depend upon priority of aspection, is a point not easily to be granted, and very hardly to be made out upon the principles of Aristotle, Alhazen, Vitello, and others, who hold that sight is made by Reception, and not by extramission; by receiving the raies of the object into the eye, and not by sending any out. (K, II, 202.)

Alhazen, whom Vitello echoes, has the image traveling in a line or ray from the object seen to the eye.[153] Aristotle agrees that "we see by the admission of something into ourselves, not by an emission,"[154] but he discards the ray theory. Instead, he

---

[151] *Historia animalium*, 585^a12.

[152] H. MacL. Currie, "Notes on Sir Thomas Browne's 'Christian Morals,' " *Notes and Queries*, New Ser., V (1958), 143, gives another use in *Christian Morals*, this time without mention of Solon, of the same idea and source in *Ethica Nicomachea*.

[153] *Opticae Thesaurus Alhazeni Arabis ... Item Vitellonis Thuringopoloni* (Basel, 1572), pp. 14, 87.

[154] *Topica*, 105^b2.

has the object to be seen exciting the transparent medium and this in turn exciting the eye.[155] Browne has lumped all three authorities together without distinction. Once more the confusion is traceable to the state in which Browne kept his commonplace books.

In another example, Aristotle and Pliny give evidence on the longevity of the deer:

> The third ground was Philosophical, and founded upon a probable Reason in Nature, that is, the defect of a Gall, which part (in the opinion of Aristotle and Pliny) this Animal wanted, and was conceived a cause and reason of their long life: according (say they) as it happeneth unto some few men, who have not this part at all. (K, II, 211.)

Aristotle approves the saying of old writers that the absence of a gall bladder conduces to longevity, but qualifies his approval by saying they had deer and solipeds in mind. He adds that the camel and dolphin also are gall-less and long-lived.[156] He also says that some men have no gall bladder,[157] but he nowhere says that men without gall bladders live a long time. Pliny says this,[158] however, and Aristotle is drawn in as well under the words "(say they)."

Browne is not always logical in his use of Aristotle. For instance, in his investigation of rightness and leftness, he writes:

> ... now unto these [the left-handed], that hand [the left hand] is properly the right, and not the other esteemed so by situation. Thus may Aristotle be made out, when he affirmeth the right claw of Crabs and Lobsters is biggest, if we take the right for the most vigorous side, and not regard the relative situation ... (K, III, 26-27.)

Aristotle does say, in *De partibus animalium*, that the right claw of spiny lobsters and crabs is invariably the larger and stronger (684a25); and he also says, in *De incessu animalium*, that the right may be defined as the more vigorous side (705a26). If, however, we apply the latter statement to the former, we get

---

[155] *Aristotle's Psychology; A Treatise on the Principles of Life (De anima and Parva naturalia)*, trans. with introduction and notes by W. A. Hammond (New York, 1902), p. xl; *De anima*, 419a12.
[156] *De partibus animalium*, 677a30.
[157] *Ibid.*, 676b31.
[158] *Natural History*, trans. J. Bostock and H. T. Riley (London, 1855-57), Bk. XI, chap. 74.

the nonsensical statement that the more vigorous claw of spiny lobsters and crabs is invariably the larger and stronger. It is evident from the latter statement and similar statements[159] that Aristotle is not applying this philosophical definition of rightness to spiny lobsters and crabs, but is making a concession to ordinary usage. In another reference Browne is willing to say that Aristotle may be "salved" in his incorrect placement of the heart on the left side since "a careless and inconsiderate aspection" or "the readiest sense of pulsation" will place it there (K, III, 13). Aristotle would probably take little comfort from such a damning, if well meant, excuse for his error. A remarkable example of illogicality is Browne's argument against the existence of the amphisbaena. Since Aristotle says that an animal with two hearts is two animals, and since we say many things of the head that he says of the heart, the amphisbaena, a serpent with a head at each end, would have to be called two animals and, so, does not exist.[160] Also, since the Aristotelian designations of parts of all animals are bottom, top, front, back, right, and left, an animal with two fronts and no back cannot exist.[161] A proper application of Browne's reasoning would rule out of existence the amoeba, the volvox, and the starfish. When he wants to prove that the number of mouths of the Nile is not definitely to be established as seven, Browne says Aristotle is so "indistinct" about the number as to call Egypt a "meer gained ground, and that by the setling of mud and limous matter brought down by the River Nilus" (K, III, 216). What this fact has to do with the number of mouths of the Nile is never clear; it is, in fact, a *non sequitur*.[162]

In three instances Browne bases arguments for the untruth of certain common reports upon the fact that Aristotle is silent about them. One is the common report that the chameleon lives on air alone (K, II, 257-258); another, that the ostrich eats iron

---

[159] *Historia animalium*, 526^{b}15, 527^{b}5; *De partibus animalium*, 684^{a}32.

[160] K, II, 234-235. Aristotle is correctly represented: determination of oneness and plurality, *De generatione animalium*, 773^{a}8; the heart as central organ, *De generatione*, 776^{b}11; *De partibus animalium*, 647^{b}5, 665^{a}11, 665^b-15, 666^{a}31, 670^{a}23, 678^{b}1.

[161] K, II, 234. *De incessu animalium*, 705^{a}26.

[162] This point has been suggested by R. R. Cawley, "Sir Thomas Browne and His Reading," *PMLA*, XLVIII (1933), 458-459.

208458

(K, II, 267-268); and the last, that the pelican opens her breast and feeds her young on her blood (K, III, 89). As Browne says, Aristotle does not mention these beliefs though he spends a great deal of space on the chameleon and ostrich,[163] and mentions the pelican several times. Browne conjectures of the first two beliefs that Aristotle omitted them as dubious or false; yet elsewhere Aristotle includes dubious material and so labels it. In fact, Browne finds fault with his master on occasion for his use of qualifying expressions like *ut aiunt*.[164] Such *argumenta ex silentio* carry with them conjectures, possibly false, about the reason for silence.

Sometimes Browne simplifies Aristotle at the expense of strict adherence to truth. He has Aristotle "affirming that Women do not spermatize, and confer a place or receptacle rather then essential principles of generation."[165] According to Aristotle, the female does not "spermatize" and does "confer a place or receptacle"; but she supplies "essential principles of generation" in the catamenia as well.[166] In *Problemata* Aristotle (or the various authors of *Problemata*) poses a question, and then suggests in interrogative form various answers to the question. At no sacrifice to the truth, Browne tends in his Latin translation to change the question into a declarative sentence by dropping the introductory "why" (K, VI, 228-229). So far he is justified, but in *Pseudodoxia epidemica* he sometimes converts one of the suggested answers into a definitive statement, putting it forth as *the* answer. For instance, Aristotle assumes that animals other than man "seldom or never" emit semen during sleep and asks whether man does so because he alone sleeps on his back (892ᵇ15). Browne simplifies Aristotle's "seldom or never" to "never" and has Aristotle attributing man's emission to his sleeping on his back (K, III, 9-10). Aristotle asks whether the fact that the senses, unlike other parts of the body, are equal on both sides is due to habit (958ᵇ12). Browne converts the query into a negative statement by Aristotle that the bilateral

---

[163] *Historia animalium*, Bk. II, chap. 11; *De partibus animalibus*, Bk. IV, chap. 14.
[164] K, II, 231; K, III, 50, 298.
[165] K, II, 246; also K, III, 309.
[166] Among many passages in *De generatione animalium*: 729ᵃ21.

equality of the senses is not due to habitual use (K, III, 22). Sometimes in various works Aristotle has loose ends that might be neatly tied together. He says that many lands now dry were formerly covered by water and, conversely, that many lands once dry have been invaded by the sea.[167] Browne makes these two sets of lands the same lands: "though in such places the ground commonly riseth, yet afterward it much sinketh" (K, VI, 342).

In some instances, the translators and commentators of Aristotle have assisted Browne in misrepresenting him. Here Browne is talking of ambidexterity: "And therefore Hippocrates, saith, that Women are not ambidextrous, that is, not so often as Men; for some are found, which indifferently make use of both. And so may Aristotle say, that only Men are ambidextrous..." (K, III, 27). Aristotle says simply, "Of all animals man alone can learn to make equal use of both hands."[168] The distinction is between man and animals, not between man and woman, as Browne has it. The Scaliger commentary to this passage in *Historia animalium* provides the key (p. 150). In it Hippocrates makes the statement that Browne gives, to the effect that women are not ambidextrous; then Scaliger makes the qualification to this statement that Browne attributes to Hippocrates, that women are not ambidextrous so often as men. Into this context, Browne introduces Aristotle's statement from the text above. However, he passes over the fact that, in this statement, Aristotle is distinguishing between man and the other animals, and not between man and woman.

In another place, Browne needs authority for a serpent with two heads, one at each end. Aristotle (*De generatione animalium*, 770[a]24) can supply him with a two-headed serpent, but says nothing about where the heads are located. Scaliger in his commentary to *Historia animalium*[169] is more helpful: "Amphisbaena parva et minime vegeto motu, capitibus binis, alterum enim loco caudae habet." Browne now combines Aristotle in *De generatione* and Scaliger in his commentary to *His-*

---

[167] *Meteorologica*, 352[a]3.
[168] *Historia animalium*, 497[b]31.
[169] P. 243 (commentary on passage about snakes in general, 505[b]5-18).

toria animalium and calls both "Aristotle": "It is not denied there have been bicipitous Serpents with the head at each extream, for an example hereof we find in Aristotle ... " (K, II, 235). The motivating force behind such distortions as these is a desire to prove the point in hand without complicating the presentation. If there were room, instances could be shown in which Browne distorts Scaliger's testimony to make it support Aristotle's,[170] and for the same reason.

In certain passages Browne takes cognizance of the dangers attendant upon blindly following translations and commentaries;[171] and, while theoretically a large proportion of his errors could be laid to the account of bad translations (a theory that cannot be tested since so few of his Latin texts are available for comparison), actually what we know of his methods of handling material points to Browne as the one responsible. In any event, he could read the Greek. In one instance the fault is clearly in Scaliger's translation. Here animals lose their hoofs in the foot sickness, "sed ungulas amittunt,"[172] and Browne quotes Scaliger (K, V, 258), whereas a more accurate modern translation has the opposite, "ac ne ungulas quidem amittunt."[173]

In his eagerness to prove his point, Browne sometimes reads more into Aristotle than the text warrants. In one place he has been listing substances that do or do not freeze: "And therefore Aristotle makes a trial of the fertility of humane seed, from the experiment of congelation; for that (saith he) which is not watery and improlifical will not conglaciate ... " (K, II, 89). In one of the two passages on the subject, in *Historia animalium* (523ª19), Aristotle says that in frosty weather semen does not "coagulate" and that its fertility may be tested by whether or not it sinks in water. In the other passage, in *De generatione animalium* (735ª34), he says that semen, unlike watery fluids, does not freeze. In neither passage is there a test

---

[170] See pp. 101 *infra*.

[171] K, II, 236, 241.

[172] *Historia animalium*, 604ª13; Scaliger edition, p. 967. In the Keynes edition of Browne, "amittunt" becomes "omittunt."

[173] Ἀριστοτέλης. *Aristotelis opera omnia. Graece et Latine* [with a preface by A. F. Didot] (Fragmenta Aristotelis collegit ... illustravit Æ. Heitz), 5 vols. (Paris, 1848-74), III, 166.

of fertility by freezing. What Browne has done is a subject of conjecture. If he read only the first passage in Aristotle, he may have made a mental substitution of freezing for flotation; or, in this same first passage, he may have applied a statement in it that fresh semen is white and consistent *if healthy* (my italics) to the statement in the next sentence that semen does not coagulate in frosty weather, and assumed from Aristotle's silence that what is not white and consistent, therefore not healthy, therefore "watery and improlifical," will freeze. If Browne read only the second passage, in *De generatione*, he may have included watery semen among watery fluids and assumed it would freeze. Once more the test of fertility by freezing must be read into the passage. If Browne read both passages, the test of fertility by freezing must still be interpolated and the possibility still applies that Browne is reading too much into Aristotle's words. One wonders also at the logic: if watery semen is "improlifical," why not let its appearance suffice for a test, especially since neither the test by appearance nor by freezing affords a direct test of its fertility, and one may know by its appearance whether or not a particular lot will freeze once the fact is established that watery semen freezes?

In another instance the discussion concerns the time needed for drowned animals to rise to the surface: "Such as are fat do commonly float soonest, for their bodies soonest ferment, and that substance approacheth nearest unto air; and this is one of Aristotle's reasons why dead Eels will not float, because saith he, they have but slender bellies, and little fat" (K, III, 31-32). Aristotle says that eels do not float because of "slender bellies" and apparently also because of "little fat";[174] thus far Browne is correct, but Aristotle does not tell how these factors operate to keep the dead eel under water. He neither says nor implies that fermentation is responsible. In fact, he says elsewhere that fatty substances are incorruptible,[175] and are not subject to decay because they contain air, which "relatively to the other elements is fire, and fire never becomes corrupted."[176] The

---

[174] *Historia animalium*, 592ª10.
[175] *Historia animalium*, 521ª1.
[176] *De longitudine et brevitate vitae*, 466ª24.

heat, and presumably the air, remaining after extraction by heat, he says in still another place, makes such oily substances as lard and suet light, and for this reason they float on the surface of other fluids.[177] Browne has read into the words of Aristotle a causation that does not agree with the latter's philosophy.

In a final instance, Browne, wishing to find as many uses of the quincunx as possible, gives as an example that "seems confirmed" the military and vineyard formation of ancient Greece "συστάδας ἀμπέλων" (K, IV, 74). Literally translated, this expression is "groupings together of the vines." Συστάς is a military term, as Browne says, to designate a formation of soldiers. Browne qualifies his statement with "seems confirmed," but even so he is reading too much into the Greek. There is no reason to believe that συστάδας ἀμπέλων are quincuncial formations; *A Greek-English Lexicon* of Liddell and Scott defines them as "vines planted closely and irregularly, not in rows."

Four principal reasons explain Browne's many mistakes in the use of Aristotle: insufficient reading, carelessness, too great reliance upon memory, and wishful thinking.

Fewer errors arise from insufficient reading than from the other reasons, and about half of the errors in this category are found in *Religio medici*, Browne's first work. There is evidence of a steady, though no very startling, growth of knowledge of Aristotle from the 1642 edition of *Religio medici* to the 1672 edition of *Pseudodoxia epidemica*. In the former, Aristotle is represented as condemning the fourth figure in logic. In later editions, possibly because of Sir Kenelm Digby's objection,[178] Browne substituted a general statement for the "fourth figure" (W, II, 108, n. 3) which is shadowed forth in *Analytica priora* (29^{a}19), but which it remained for Galen to develop. The statement to the effect that Hippocrates is mentioned only once in Aristotle was taken from the commonplace books and inserted unchanged into the 1672 edition of *Pseudodoxia* (K, II, 46), and, so, represents a new use of knowledge acquired earlier. Not all added knowledge is accurate. The statement about the heating of arrowheads and bullets in flight, mistakenly attrib-

---

[177] *De partibus animalium*, 672^{a}6.
[178] *Observations upon Religio Medici* (London, 1643); W, II, 148-149.

uted to "Meteors," was first added to *Pseudodoxia* in the 1650 edition (K, II, 151). In connection with another subject, the 1646 and 1650 editions of *Pseudodoxia* state: "Aristotle, in the second of his *Meteors*, speaks lightly thereof, ὥσπερ μυθολογοῦσι, and esteemeth thereof as a fable,"[179] which in the later editions becomes: "Aristotle in the second of his *Meteors* speaks lightly thereof, ὥσπερ μυθολογοῦσι, which word is variously rendred, by some as a fabulous account, by some as a common talk" (K, III, 306). Evidently Browne looked more closely after 1650 at the translations of the Greek in the Latin editions of *Meteorologica*.

Carelessness and too great reliance upon memory, which may be considered together, are no doubt responsible for many of the statements erroneously attributed to Aristotle, improper designations of a particular work as source, statements that cover too much or too little, inaccurate lumping together of sources, oversimplification, and other errors.

Wishful thinking comes into play in many of these types of errors when Browne is anxious to use Aristotle to prove a point and the evidence does not quite fit. His memory of the material and his logic are not strong enough to make him reject it. For instance: he is writing of the efficacy of the sun. Aristotle recommends that cities be open toward the east. What is the intention, to catch the wind or the sun? Perhaps it is the sun. It must be the sun (K, III, 211).[180]

CONCLUSION

We come now to the conclusion of this study. As we have seen earlier, Browne gives no evidence of having read many of Aristotle's works; yet he makes several statements covering all of them. Aristotle, he says, never mentions the basilisk (K, II, 199) or the story that the pelican opens her breast to feed her young (K, III, 89). The Stagirite also says nothing of the

---

[179] *Pseudodoxia Epidemica: or, Enquiries into Very Many Received Tenents, and Commonly Presumed Truths* (London, 1646), p. 369; 2nd ed. (London, 1650), p. 315.

[180] Rosalie L. Colie, "Dean Wren's Marginalia and Early Science at Oxford," *Bodleian Library Record*, VI (1960), 544, notes in a copy of the 1646 *Pseudodoxia epidemica* comments by the father of Sir Christopher Wren deploring various inadequacies in Browne's scholarship.

belief that the chameleon lives on air alone (K, II, 257-258) or that the ostrich can digest iron (K, II, 267-268).[181] The word *Zizania* never appears in Aristotle (K, V, 53). Hippocrates' name appears only once in Aristotle's works (K, II, 46). These statements, all of them accurate, suggest four possibilities: (1) that Browne went for his information to the most likely works of Aristotle and was fortunate enough, at least in these instances, to conclude accurately that he need not look elsewhere; (2) that he found these statements in reliable authors who had made a special study of Aristotle; (3) that he read all of Aristotle thoroughly with a careful watch for certain items; and (4) that he had an efficient system of indexing in individual works, lexicons, and the like.

The first possibility has evidence to support it. Browne's method of statement might well indicate that he went to the passage where Aristotle treats the chameleon and did not find what he wanted: "Aristotle distinctly treating hereof, hath made no mention of this remarkable propriety ... " (K, II, 258). The same is true of Browne's statement about the ostrich: "For Aristotle and Oppianus who have particularly treated hereof are silent in this singularity ... " (K, II, 268). For his statement about chiromancy quoted earlier,[182] thorough reading of one work, or use of its index, is his method; and he has indeed overlooked material on the subject elsewhere. The basilisk and the pelican, subjects of other general statements, are also animal forms and, so, inquiry about them might with reasonable safety be confined to the animal books, with which Browne was familiar. On the other hand, his statement that Aristotle mentions Hippocrates only once is one that any unsearched work of Aristotle might falsify; yet it is correct, as are the other general statements set down in the second paragraph above.

The second possibility, that he found such statements in reliable authors who had made a particular study of Aristotle, is true in at least one instance. Speaking of the tides of Euripus, he says, "For, as Vicomercatus and others observe, he [Aristotle] hath made no mention hereof in his Works ... " (K, III, 298).

---

181 See pp. 91-92 *supra*.
182 K, I, 75, quoted on pp. 84-85 *supra*.

The third possibility, that he read and made notes on all of Aristotle, seems least likely of all in view of his not making any use or mention of fourteen of Aristotle's works and in view of his not-always-reliable scholarship in general. The commonplace books, in which he recorded observations from his reading, show sporadic rather than systematic scholarship.

The last possibility, that Browne resorted to some efficient system of indexing, has a great deal of evidence to support it. He could find indexes bound in with the individual works of Aristotle. When he wanted to set down "particulars *De Cervis* out of Aristotle & Scaliger" (K, VI, 175) for Edward's benefit, he might turn to the *Elenchus verborum et rerum in hoc opere summe notandarum* in the back of Scaliger and find "cervi descriptio et natura 254." The search for materials in individual works, mentioned above, may apply here too; that is, Browne may have used the index, instead of reading through each work. The form of statement in one instance in which he brings together material from two works of Aristotle makes it seem likely that he conducted his search by individual works: "Aristotle besides the frequent undervaluing of his authority, in his Books of Animals gives him [Ctesias the Cnidian] the lie no less than twice, concerning the seed of Elephants" (K, II, 57). Aristotle gives Ctesias the lie about the seed of elephants exactly twice, in *Historia animalium* (523^{a}26) and in *De generatione animalium* (736^{a}2), but Browne's method of statement protects him in case other instances that he does not know about—in other works—are found. However, in addition to indexes in individual works, he may have used a more comprehensive index. The statements that apply to all of Aristotle may be explained in this light, as well as the various statements in which Browne has coalesced material from more than one work of Aristotle.[183] Of course, we must allow for the possibility that he came upon related data in Aristotle separately and at various times and with continuity of interest recorded them in the commonplace books; but there are instances that give evidence of the use of one or more Greek lexicon-concordances to supply references not only to Aristotle but to other authors of

---

[183] K, II, 57, 179, 298; K, III, 27, 298.

antiquity. In one place Browne lists four Greek words for lying down at meals and says they are used in this sense in "Aristotle, Athenaeus, Euripides, Sophocles, and all humane Authors" (K, III, 105). In another he says that the "proper signification" of ἀκρίς as locust is to be found in Origen, Jerome, Chrysostom, Hilary, Ambrose, the Septuagint, "Greek vocabularies," and Suidas; and that the word is used in a similar sense by Aristotle, Dioscorides, Galen, "and several humane Authors" (K, III, 285). In still another place he says the word *Zizania* is "not mention'd in other parts of Scripture, nor in any ancient Greek Writer: it is not to be found in Aristotle, Theophrastus, or Dioscorides" (K, V, 53). The *Lexicon* of Suidas does not seem to be the source of such statements, but lexicons of the same type are evidently the "vocabularies" in question. Some such "vocabularies," sporadically used, may have allowed Browne to make his sweeping generalizations. He probably did not use indexes consistently. For the most part, he seems to have read widely in the Stagirite's work and recorded what interested him in the commonplace books, classifying to make future reference easy.

When Browne sits down to write *Pseudodoxia epidemica*, or a letter to Edward, he has before him not only the works of various authors and perhaps lexicons, but the commonplace books in which he has noted the words and ideas of many authors. He must work rapidly if he is not to be frustrated by the "importunity of uroscopy." If a passage or idea is set down in the commonplace books, he takes it from them. If not, he tries his capacious memory and sets down his recollection of the words or thought as best he can. Definite and exact reference and textual fidelity do not particularly concern him. If memory will not serve, he plies the index or opens by guess to a well-thumbed page and begins to read and write. If the first passage he strikes contains what he wishes, he generally looks no further to see whether another passage is better stated or inconsistent.

He usually reads the text and the commentary together. On one particular day, after reading Aristotle's list of kinds of hawks in Book IX, chapter 36 of *Historia animalium*,[184] he

---

[184] 620ᵃ17; the list is referred to in K, V, 75.

glances at the commentary to the passage[185] and is disappointed, but pounces upon this cross reference: "De his omnibus generibus sententiam nostram explicavimus supra in Secundo." Turning back to Book II, he finds a lengthy commentary about hawks attached to chapter 15.[186] He skims through it, making note of a detail here and there, until his eye is caught near the middle of the commentary by the remarkable performance of King Henry's hawk, which Scaliger saw strike down "a Buzzard, two wild Geese, divers Kites, a Crane and a Swan" (K, V, 75). As he writes *Pseudodoxia epidemica*, he often cites or quotes text and commentary together, sometimes with little or no discrimination.[187] He plays text and commentary off against each other. Sometimes, as we have seen, Scaliger's commentary helps Browne give a wrench to Aristotle's meaning that will make it just fit what he has in mind.[188] But Scaliger can be served in the same fashion. When Aristotle gives the short period of gestation and the short youth of deer as proof of their not being long-lived,[189] Scaliger comments, "But this is false if you take the arguments apart."[190] Browne gives a twist to Scaliger's meaning and says, "And these, saith Scaliger, are good Mediums conjunctively taken, that is, not one without the other" (K, II, 207). Sometimes the commentary supplies more than Browne acknowledges. An Arabian bird that builds its nest of cinnamon is, says Browne, "by Herodotus called *Cinnamulgus*, and by Aristotle, *Cinnamomus;* and as a fabulous conceit is censured by Scaliger" (K, II, 220). Aristotle details the habits of the bird, saying nothing of its particular habitat and citing no authority.[191] Scaliger not only "censures" the "fabulous conceit," but he supplies Arabia, Herodotus, and

---

[185] Scaliger edition, p. 1080. The chapter numbers above are those of the Oxford translation (cited in note 125 *supra*), usually differing somewhat from Scaliger's.

[186] 506a12; the commentary, pp. 247-253 of Scaliger's edition.

[187] As on K, II, 179, where he mingles material on the elephant from *De incessu animalium* (709a9) and *Historia animalium* (498a8) with material from Scaliger's commentary on *Historia*, p. 153.

[188] See pp. 93-94 *supra*.

[189] *Historia animalium*, 578b23.

[190] P. 770 of Scaliger edition.

[191] *Historia animalium*, 616a7.

Cinnamulgus.[192] Generally, however, Browne clearly distinguishes and fairly represents the contributions of Aristotle and Scaliger.

As he reads and takes notes, Browne is summarizing now, and he skips along, taking a phrase here and a fact or idea there. Anything commonplace or abstruse he is likely to skip. He has not the time for mastery. Any picture of Browne as an antiquarian recluse working outside of time and the world must be dismissed for one of a man writing with one hand and compounding an electuary with the other.[193] Chapter numbers and page numbers take up time better spent with the slit-eared Arginusa deer. Also, they damage the smooth flow and lyrical cadences of his prose. He had best just set down "Aristotle" with a fresh turn of assertion and go on. Now his attention wanders. He reads about the "Coa" and "Chia," leg bones of cattle, suddenly remembers an ancient dice game played with these bones, and, indulging his whim, he works the dice motif into Scaliger's Latin (W, IV, 298). With *De partibus animalium* open before him to chapter 2 of Book IV, he reads that the deer has no gall, writes this fact down, and continues composition. Then, glancing back at Aristotle a few lines below the first reference to the deer, he sees that the camel also has no gall; and this fact too goes into *Pseudodoxia* (K, II, 211). In a letter to Edward he includes a practical suggestion about the care of Edward's baby, who is in danger of becoming too fat. He copies out an appropriate passage from *Historia animalium* on the subject of mother's milk and adds a comment of Scaliger. Then his eye is caught by an unusual fact and mother's milk is forgotten; the cows of Epirus, says Aristotle, are so large that the shepherd has to stand up to milk them. Perhaps they are buffaloes, Browne muses (K, VI, 220-221).

Suggestions flow in from the stream of associations. The *anima* of Aristotle is ἐντελέχεια, whose Latin translation is *actus*. Yes, and *actus perspicui* is Aristotle's definition of light (W, II, 14-15). Fermentation causes dead bodies to float; addled eggs

---

[192] P. 1049 of Scaliger edition.
[193] Cf. Peter Green, *Sir Thomas Browne* (booklet in "Bibliographical Series of Supplements to 'British Book News' on Writers and Their Work," No. 108) (London, 1959), p. 28.

float, also sterile seeds. And Aristotle tests the fertility of human seed by flotation (K, III, 32). Finally, Browne tires of composition. He turns the pages of Aristotle at random, and records in his commonplace books the things that interest him as a man of curiosity and a physician. When he has time, he will investigate the truth of these things for himself.

Along with the disparagements of Browne's hit-or-miss scholarship, a word should be spoken for the other side of the ledger. If we look at his changes in quotations in the light of the seventeenth-century attitude toward such matters—an attitude shared by so meticulous a scholar as Milton—that a writer heedful of style and brevity should reshape the raw material of quotation, almost three fourths of Browne's citations and quotations of Aristotle represent the original with a reasonable degree of accuracy. Sometimes he works carefully with the Greek and Latin text to ensure absolute accuracy. And, where his memory and scribal failings have not betrayed him, his textual changes show a grasp of effective composition in Latin and even, to some extent, in Greek. He has long been regarded as one of the foremost English prose stylists. It now appears that he is enough of a Latin scholar to correct Scaliger, just as that other great English scholar of the century, Milton, presumed to correct Claudius Salmasius.

*

Sir Thomas Browne
and His Reading

*

I

IN THIS STUDY[1] the aim will be to concentrate on the particular parts of Sir Thomas Browne's reading that best reveal the workings of his mind; no attempt will be made to cover the whole of his voluminous reading.

In the past thirty years or so, scholars have studied various aspects of the subject and have emphasized books that they felt had some influence, direct or indirect, in shaping Browne's own judgments. Olivier Leroy, for instance, in 1931 stressed again the Bible and its peripheral literature such as the Talmud and Targum and the work of Philo Judaeus himself.[2] Leroy goes on to call attention to the commentators such as Hugo Grotius, Daniel Heinsius, and Johann Buxtorf and to refer us to the sermons and meditations which Browne himself says that he was reading. He next treats the Platonic element, showing Sir Thomas' natural sympathy for the philosopher's ideas and those of his successors such as Marsilio Ficino. On the more scientific side, he shows the possible impact of Paracelsus' *Archidoxes*,[3] of Cornelius Agrippa,

---

[1] The study reproduces in large part an article by the author that appeared in *PMLA*. "Sir Thomas Browne and His Reading," *PMLA*, XLVIII, 426-470.

[2] *Le Chevalier Thomas Browne: Médecin, Styliste et Métaphysicien* (Paris, 1931). See especially pp. 225-240.

[3] Oxford, 1661.

and of the Paracelsian Robert Fludd. Without going into detail, Leroy brings in the names of Andreas Vesalius, Daniel Sennert, Lazare Rivière, and Thomas Bartholin, and of such travelers as Du Loir, Jan van Linschoten, Joannes de Laet, Antonio Pigafetta, Jean Baptiste Tavernier, and the widely read George Sandys, author of *A Relation of a Journey*.[4]

Also in 1931, Professor Alwin Thaler published an article[5] dealing with Browne's use of his immediate predecessors. Quite frankly granting that the allusions to many are stray and casual, Professor Thaler introduces such names as Sir Philip Sidney, John Donne, Sir Walter Ralegh, John Foxe, Bishop Joseph Hall, William Camden, Edmund Spenser, Michael Drayton, Ben Jonson, and the translators Philemon Holland and Sir Thomas North. His main contention is that, in an attempt to prove Browne a medievalist, scholars have tended to neglect the fact that he was well read in his near contemporaries. Thaler concludes his article with six pages of parallels between Sir Thomas and Francis Bacon.

Gordon K. Chalmers made important contributions to the subject in his thesis submitted in 1933.[6] It is most unfortunate that his early death should have prevented publication of this thesis.[7] He was one of the first to use the rare *Catalogue of the Libraries of the Learned Sir Thomas Brown, and Dr. Edward Brown, His Son*[8] as an effective checklist. The upshot of Chalmers' work is that he proves Browne was usually up-to-date in his science. Though he concedes that Sir Thomas read Bacon carefully, he draws sharp distinctions between their minds.

---

[4] 2nd ed.; London, 1621.

[5] "Sir Thomas Browne and the Elizabethans," *Studies in Philology*, XXVIII (1931), 87 ff. Two years previously Thaler had treated the relation of Browne to Shakespeare in *Shakespere's Silences* (Cambridge, Mass., 1929), pp. 97 ff.

[6] Unpublished dissertation, "Sir Thomas Browne's Thought and Its Relation to Contemporary Ideas," 3 vols. (Harvard, 1933).

[7] Parts of it have appeared in various places. See "Hieroglyphs and Sir Thomas Browne," *Virginia Quarterly Review*, XI (1935), 547-560; "Sir Thomas Browne, True Scientist," *Osiris*, II (1936), 28-79; "Three Terms of the Corpuscularian Philosophy," *Modern Philology*, XXXIII (1936), 243 ff.; "The Lodestone and the Understanding of Matter in Seventeenth Century England," *Philosophy of Science*, IV (1937), 75 ff.

[8] London, 1711.

Browne allowed more place to hypothesis. Whereas Bacon was interested in phenomena, Browne was primarily interested in ideas. Bacon's efforts were essentially utilitarian; Browne was merely seeking the *truth*. Bacon followed the particular action, while Sir Thomas probed for the general principle behind it. Sir Francis concerned himself with efficient causes, Browne with final causes. With all of this, Chalmers grants that Browne's method was more Baconian than Cartesian; and he points to even clearer distinctions, while at the same time acknowledging that throughout his literary career Sir Thomas probably had a thorough familiarity with Descartes' writings.[9] Whereas the Frenchman proceeded by strict logic, Browne's reason is always joined to sense. Also, Descartes was obviously impatient of pursuing truth by experiment. Actually, Chalmers argues, "Boyle's Corpuscularean Philosophy comes closer than any other system to outlining the physical world which Sir Thomas Browne thought of and studied."[10] Dr. Chalmers traces the theory of "magnetical philosophy" from Greek times down, laying particular emphasis naturally on William Gilbert's *De magnete*[11] and showing how Browne used Athanasius Kircher's *De arte magnetica*[12] in the second edition (1650) of *Pseudodoxia*.[13] To a certain extent Sir Thomas went along with the atomist Pierre Gassendi.[14] Finally, as Chalmers notices, in later editions he made use of Robert Hooke's *Micrographia*;[15] and, in hieroglyphics, he inevitably relied in part on those two old dependables Horapollo and J. Pierius.

Another study that emphasizes Browne's dependence on William Gilbert's *De magnete* is Dewey K. Ziegler's *In Divided and Distinguished Worlds: Religion and Rhetoric in the Writings of*

---

[9] Many of Descartes' works are listed in *A Catalogue of the Libraries*, referred to above.
[10] Unpublished dissertation, "Sir Thomas Browne's Thought ...," 3 vols. (Harvard, 1933), II, 165.
[11] London, 1600.
[12] Rome, 1641.
[13] "Sir Thomas Browne, True Scientist," *Osiris*, II (1936), 37.
[14] E. S. Merton, *Science and Imagination in Sir Thomas Browne* (New York, 1949), p. 84, believes that Browne did not follow the school of atomistic embryology, of which Gassendi was an important exponent.
[15] London, 1665.

Sir Thomas Browne.[16] But Ziegler perceives Sir Kenelm Digby also behind Sir Thomas' theory of electric attraction. And for him Bacon and Descartes reenter the picture. The main stress, however, the book's penchant being what it is, is laid upon Plato and the Neoplatonists. Ziegler sees a close connection with Hermes Trismegistus and he contends that Hermetic philosophy was in Browne's mind continually.[17] The mystical writings of the Hebrew cabalists, as well as the rabbinical authors in general, left their mark.

E. S. Merton, in a book published in 1949,[18] pursues the tendency of Chalmers to play down the Baconian and Cartesian elements in Browne. On the other hand, he is inclined to play up the Aristotelian influence.[19] He calls attention to two works of Lord Herbert of Cherbury that, he says, have not had their due—*De veritate*[20] and *De causis errorum*[21]—and draws an analogy between Browne's thinking and Herbert's "common notions."[22] Merton makes a special point of Sir Thomas' scientific interests having become increasingly biological;[23] and he mentions in particular Nathaniel Highmore's *History of Generation.*[24] Indeed, he says, Paracelsus,[25] Hieronymus Fabricius, and Jan Baptista van Helmont play an important part in the formation of Browne's theories. At times Merton resorts to justifiable list making, as when considering the authorities most frequently referred to in *Pseudodoxia*: Pliny, Aristotle, Julius Caesar Scaliger, Galen, Ulyssis Aldrovandi, Konrad von Gesner, Pierre Belon, Aelian, Albertus Magnus, the Bible, Antonio M. Brasavola, Pietro A. Mattioli, Girolamo Cardano, Boetius, Athanasius Kircher, Herodotus, Plutarch, and Paracelsus. Browne, he says,

---

[16] Cambridge, Mass., 1943.
[17] *Ibid.*, p. 34.
[18] *Science and Imagination in Sir Thomas Browne* (New York, 1949). See especially pp. 18-30.
[19] *Ibid.*, p. 12.
[20] Paris, 1624.
[21] London, 1645.
[22] *Op. cit.*, pp. 29, 91, 139, and 141.
[23] *Op. cit.*, pp. 11 ff. and 136.
[24] London, 1651.
[25] *Op. cit.*, p. 148.

read Epicurus and Lucretius without any great sympathy for their general philosophies.[26]

Like Chalmers and Merton, Professor Finch emphasizes the influence of William Gilbert, Descartes, and Kenelm Digby in forming Browne's theory of magnetic action.[27] Another famous scientist who played a determining part was William Harvey, and Finch quite properly stresses the *De generatione*,[28] which Sir Thomas recommended to his physician son Edward, as well as the better known *De motu cordis*.[29] Finch also uses the evidence of *A Catalogue of the Libraries*, referred to above, while arguing for the influence of such men as Ulyssis Aldrovandi, Konrad von Gesner, Guillaume Rondelet, and Elias Ashmole (whose *Theatrum chemicum Britannicum* was published at London in 1652). He makes some point of Browne's awareness of Rabelais during his Montpellier sojourn, calling attention to the often-ignored fact that the creator of Pantagruel and Gargantua was by profession a doctor.[30] In discussing *The Garden of Cyrus*, Finch adds the names of Benoit Court and G. B. della Porta.[31]

Three unpublished dissertations I have not read, and the dissertation abstracts do not make clear their contributions to the subject of Browne's reading. The first is Ruth M. V. Kieft's "The Nineteenth Century Reputation of Sir Thomas Browne" (University of Michigan, 1957) (*DA*, XVIII, 2151). The second is Donald F. Rauber's "Sir Thomas Browne: A Study in the Middle Way (University of Oregon, 1958) (*DA*, XVIII, 236). Rauber concentrates largely on *Religio medici* and holds that the *via media* of such thinkers as William Laud, William Chillingworth,

---

[26] See also Merton's article, "Sir Thomas Browne's Scientific Quest," *Journal of the History of Medicine*, III (1948), 214-228. He has published further results of his scientific researches in "The Botany of Sir Thomas Browne," *Isis*, XLVII (1956), 161-171, and in "Sir Thomas Browne on Astronomy," *History of Ideas News Letter*, IV (1958), 83-86.

[27] Jeremiah S. Finch, *Sir Thomas Browne: A Doctor's Life of Science and Faith* (New York, 1950).

[28] *Exercitationes de generatione animalium* (Amsterdam, 1651).

[29] *Exercitatio anatomica de motu cordis et sanguinis in animalibus* (Frankfurt, 1628).

[30] *Op. cit.*, pp. 61-62. Perhaps some significance is to be read into the fact that one of the subjects Rabelais seems to have interested himself in as a physician was syphilis.

[31] *Op. cit.*, p. 188.

Jeremy Taylor, Richard Hooker, and Donne "equates perfectly with Browne's system of balances." The last thesis is Leonard I. Nathanson's "The Strategy of Truth: A Study of Sir Thomas Browne's *Religio Medici*" (University of Wisconsin, 1959) (*DA*, XX, 2295). Nathanson naturally emphasizes Plato and Platonic Christianity, and he, like Rauber, draws the analogy with Chillingworth and Jeremy Taylor.

II

Any student of the works of Sir Thomas Browne comes soon to realize how wide was his reading, especially during the years he spent at Norwich. His interests ranged over a broad field and included, naturally, foreign lands. His various books, notably *Pseudodoxia epidemica*, reveal that he studied and thought much about France and Italy, about Egypt and the Holy Land, even about India and China.[32]

The problem of defining the extent of his reading about those countries—the problem we are about to undertake—is a highly complicated one for several reasons. In the first place, we have here to deal with a man who handled many foreign languages at will; his good friend John Whitefoot once referred to his having "understood most of the European languages, viz. all that are in Hutter's bible."[33] His professional sojourns in Montpellier, Padua, and Leyden had presumably made him almost as familiar with French, Italian, and Dutch as with his native English, while Latin was of course his foster language. He quotes Greek readily; and German, Spanish, Portuguese, Danish, and Hebrew he knew to some extent.[34]

---

[32] Olivier Leroy, in a footnote, lists some important travelers whose works Browne read. See *Le Chevalier Thomas Browne: Médecin, Styliste et Métaphysicien* (Paris, 1931), p. 231, n. 2.

[33] *Sir Thomas Browne's Works, Including His Life and Correspondence*, ed. Simon Wilkin, 4 vols. (London, 1835-36), I, xlv. Unless otherwise specified, all further references to the *Works* in this study will be to this edition. Geoffrey Keynes issued a beautiful edition of Browne's works, without notes, in six volumes, *The Works of Sir Thomas Browne* (London, 1928-31).

[34] Browne says himself: "...besides the jargon and *patois* of several provinces, I understand no less than six languages." *Works*, II, 103-104. He probably means *modern* languages. French, of course, is taken for

But besides these valuable linguistic resources, Sir Thomas had human "feelers" that put him in contact with the remotest countries; his letters are fairly full of requests to traveling friends that they bring back information and specimens. "This is the account of Mr. L'Escaillot, minister in Norwich, my loving friend, who dyed in the Indies, and so I lost the antiquities and varities [rarities?] which hee had obtained for mee."[35] But before his premature death, L'Escaillot had dispatched to his "deare Browne" valuable reports about the Mogul's country, fragments of which are to be found embedded in *Pseudodoxia epidemica*.[36] Further, we have a precious page of the speculations that Browne begged some unknown friend to verify in his travels through Greenland.[37] He was, we know, acquainted with Sir Hamon L'Estrange, an adventurer for the Northwest Passage and an explorer in Ceylon;[38] with the much-traveled Paston family;[39] and with Theodore Jonas, Lutheran minister at Hitterdale, who sent long and learned screeds about Iceland to "Vir Humanis-

---

granted; reading a book like *Les voyages du sieur Du Loir* (Paris, 1654) was for him like reading English. He quotes the Italian of Giovanni Botero and translates accurately. *Works*, III, 334. He records having consulted Juan de Pineda's *Monarchia ecclesiastica*, 4 vols. (Salamanca, 1588) "in Spanish." *Works*, I, 204. With German he was apparently less familiar: "I could make a shift to understand the Duch writing in it [the fountain in Salzburg]." *Works*, I, 177. We should not, however, forget John Whitefoot's testimony about his knowledge of "most of the European languages, viz. all that are in Hutter's bible." *Works*, I, xlv. Edmund W. Gosse, *Sir Thomas Browne* (New York, 1905), p. 115, refers to his quoting Danish, Greek, and Hebrew, we can assume on Whitefoot's authority. And Latin, like French, is taken for granted. For fuller discussion of this subject, see A. C. Howell, "A Note on Sir Thomas Browne's Knowledge of Languages," *Studies in Philology*, XXII (1925), 412-417.

[35] *Works*, I, 442. Cf. also I, 246: "It was brought from the East Indies by order from Mr. Tho. Peirce, who liveth near Norwich, 1663, who gave mee some divers yeares agoe."

[36] It seems likely that Browne took from L'Escaillot hints about the annual overflow of various rivers. Cf. that gentleman's letter, *Works*, I, 440-441, with Browne's discussion, *Works*, III, 252.

[37] *Works*, IV, 375.

[38] *Works*, I, 369-370 and n. 6. Sir Hamon was the father of Sir Roger L'Estrange, the early journalist.

[39] His particular friend was Sir Robert Paston. They corresponded between 1662 and 1674. For specimens of their letters, see *Works*, I, 409-411. Francis Blomefield describes Paston as "a person of good learning, who, travelling into foreign countrys, collected many considerable rarities and curiosities." *Norfolk*, 11 vols. (London, 1805-10), III, 699.

sime" and "Vir Reverende et Doctissime."[40] It would, in fact, be difficult to overestimate the extent of the information thus assembled by a man who made a fetish of his friendships, as Browne indubitably did.[41]

From one last personal source, this time from a closer than friend, he probably derived more material than from a combination of the others.[42] His oldest son, Edward, who was to adopt his own profession, was fortunate in having traveled through most of the European countries, through France, Italy, Holland, Belgium, Austria, Hungary, Bohemia, Germany, with an excursion to Larissa in Thessaly, this last strictly against parental orders.[43] The correspondence between father and son, which

---

[40] *Works*, IV, 256-269.

[41] W. P. Dunn in *Sir Thomas Browne: A Study in Religious Philosophy* (Menasha, Wis., 1926; a second edition appeared in 1950), pp. 11-12, unaccountably maintained that Browne had fewer personal contacts than we might expect. There is much evidence that his contacts were many and close. John Whitefoot, who claimed, in "Some Minutes for the Life of Sir Thomas Browne" in *Posthumous Works of the Learned Sir Thomas Browne, Kt.* (London, 1712), to have known Browne more intimately "than any other Man, that is now left alive" (p. xxvii), said that "he was frequently and personally visited" by the greatest men of this nation (p. xxv). And there is somehow a ring of conviction about Browne's statement: "I have loved my friend, as I do virtue, my soul, my God. . . . When I am from him, I am dead till I be with him." *Works*, II, 99. He was doctor and close friend to Bishop Joseph Hall and to Arthur Dee, "who resided for many years on terms of the kindest friendship with Browne at Norwich." *Works*, I, xcv. In his correspondence, expressions of affection on both sides indicate relations warm and personal. L'Escaillot, for example, is "my loving friend" and Sir Thomas is "deare Browne" (an address indicating far more intimacy than today). His dedications are full of such addresses as "my worthy and honoured friend Nicholas Bacon" (a neighbor of his) (*Works*, III, 381); "my worthy friend M. Goodier" (p. 382); "Sir Edmund Bacon prime baronet, my true and noble friend" (p. 384); and "that true gentleman, Sir Horatio Townshend, my honoured friend" (p. 452). These can hardly all have been flourishes.

[42] Sir Thomas refers in one place to a gold medallion worth a thousand pounds "as I am informed by an ocular witness, who had a sight thereof, at Vienna, in 1669." *Works*, IV, 285. In British Museum MS. Sloan 1829, which contains this passage, we find that Browne has scribbled on the page opposite (fol. 53 verso), "my sonne Dr. Ed. Browne." Wilkin was usually careful to include such references in footnotes; in this case he failed to do so.

[43] "Beleeve it," Browne had written, "no excursion into Pol. Hung. or Turkey addes advantage or reputation unto a schollar." *Works*, I, 166. And the bad boy apologized abjectly: "I would willingly set downe something

was a notably active one and of which much has survived, is replete with questions and answers about foreign customs.[44] "Endeavor by all means to see his treasure of rarities, and what is remarkable in any private custodie."[45] There is some evidence that, when Sir Thomas himself was sojourning on the Continent, he stuck pretty closely to his knitting. And his searching inquiries of Edward seem to carry a kind of regret, a wistful desire to make up in his later days for omissions of the earlier, by traveling vicariously.

Browne was fortunate, moreover, in having the sort of memory that retained various impressions and that served him like a photographic plate in recording, once and for all, every least detail. Whitefoot, who knew him best, says he "remembered all that was remarkable in any book that he had read."[46] At seventy-three he could recall perfectly a book that he had examined "above thirtie years ago," so perfectly that he could turn away the book agent with the offhand criticism that "it containes not many plants."[47] And, two years before his death, he remembered having seen an "oestrige" "in the latter end of king James his dayes, at Greenwich, when I was a schoolboy."[48]

This gift of a really extraordinary memory, coupled with many and close contacts, is a factor which requires that we should proceed with caution in determining Browne's debt to books. Fortunately we have, for assistance in this latter task, an invaluable little volume of which there are only four copies in the world, *A Catalogue of the Libraries of the Learned Sir Thomas Brown, and Dr. Edward Brown, His Son,* referred to

---

more of my Turkish journey; but the consideration of my rashnesse and obstinate folly in undertaking it, renders my thoughts of it unpleasing." *Works*, I, 194.

[44] Long extracts from Edward's letters are to be found copied out in Sir Thomas' handwriting. British Museum MS. Sloan 1849, for example, contains a whole page of notes about the unicorn (fol. 13), obviously taken from Edward. See also the latter's *A Brief Account of Some Travels* (London, 1685), p. 101. Browne used some of Edward's notes in his chapter "Of the Unicorn's Horn." *Works*, II, 498-503. There is much valuable material from Edward's letters, particularly in British Museum MS. Sloan 1911-13, that Wilkin left unprinted.

[45] *Works*, I, 177.
[46] *Works*, I, xliii.
[47] *Works*, I, 251.
[48] *Works*, I, 281.

above.[49] But even with this, we must not presume too far. Edward was much narrower in interests than his great father,[50] and considerable tampering with the library must have gone on between Sir Thomas' death in 1682 and January 1710/11, the date of the sale for which the *Catalogue of the Libraries* was issued.[51] It should be noted that a list that contains no set of Shakespeare, no Richard Knolles's *Generall Historie of the Turkes*,[52] no John Greaves's *Pyramidographia*,[53] and no Prosper Alpinus on the medical practice of the Egyptians,[54] can scarcely be said to represent the library of Sir Thomas Browne. Though the list may, therefore, and indeed must, be used as partially confirmatory, our evidence should be based in the first instance on his actual knowledge of the sources as revealed in his works.

Before attempting to determine the manner of his use of those sources, we should get quite clearly in mind certain fundamental traits of the man as they reflect light upon his literary habits. We must recognize first that Sir Thomas contains within himself as many contradictions as his favorite book, the Bible. There is the Browne who liked to let his mind soar into mystical visions. "I love," he says, "to lose myself in a mystery; to pursue my reason to an *O altitudo!*"[55] There is also the Browne who made such a painstaking collection of minute specimens that the diarist John Evelyn wondered at his meticulous industry.[56] There is again the Browne of the *Religio medici*, and the Browne who practiced medicine for forty-six successful years in Norwich.

---

[49] London, 1711. The book is an octavo of 58 pages, containing 2,377 lots. For a full description, see Geoffrey Keynes, *A Bibliography of Sir Thomas Browne* (Cambridge, 1924), pp. 182-184.

[50] This fact accounts for his having fitted perfectly into the Royal Society whereas his far more versatile father knocked at its doors in vain. Some of the letters that best illustrate this narrowness were not printed by Wilkin. Edward was quite capable of setting down long lists of things observed, uninterpreted and untransformed by his imagination. British Museum MS. Sloan 1911-13 contains several such lists.

[51] Geoffrey Keynes surmises that "the greater part of the collection had been formed by Sir Thomas himself." *A Bibliography of Sir Thomas Browne* (Cambridge, 1924), p. 182.

[52] 3rd ed.; London, 1621.

[53] London, 1646.

[54] *De medicina Aegyptiorum* (Paris, 1645).

[55] *Works*, II, 13.

[56] *Works*, I, xciv.

Indeed, so self-contradictory is he that there are few things that can be definitely set down and called his, in which he unalterably believes. Immortality is one, surely. And monarchy is, less surely, another. But though it seems next to impossible to categorize him, it is quite possible to indicate very definite leanings. And one of these is his preference for the microscope over the telescope. He was always more concerned with the microcosm than the macrocosm. "We carry with us the wonders we seek without us: there is all Africa and her prodigies in us."[57] This leaning explains his preference for William Harvey over Columbus,[58] and for William Gilbert over Vespucci.[59] It is responsible for his corresponding with the alchemist Sir Robert Paston[60] and the astrologer William Lilly,[61] and for his friendship with such converts to the new alchemy as Arthur Dee and Kenelm Digby.

Considering this predilection, we should hardly expect to find him deeply interested in what we might call the broader aspects of foreign travel. He does not concern himself, for example, with the laws of other countries, with their governments, or with such living problems as colonization. Nor does he discuss their literatures as purveyors of national characteristics. He does, to be sure, let his imagination play over certain chimerical notions with regard to the future of America and the East;[62] but these are scarcely more than fancies, exemplifying rather his mystical penchant for extravagant prophecies than any well-reasoned conjectures about future states. Usually, we find him culling odd details such as the pensile tomb of Mahomet, the names of fish in the sea of Tiberias, lions in the Prince of Bavaria's court, talkative elephants, magnetical rocks, and vegetable horns.

---

[57] *Works*, II, 21.
[58] "And be sure you make yourself master of Dr. Harvey's piece *De Circul. Sang.*; which discovery I prefer to that of Columbus." *Works*, I, 356.
[59] "And this was the invention of D. Gilbert, not many years past, a physician in London. And therefore, although some assume the invention of its direction, and other have had the glory of the card, yet in the experiments, grounds, and causes thereof, England produced the father philosopher, and discovered more in it, than Columbus or Americus did ever by it." *Works*, II, 298-299.
[60] *Works*, I, xcvi and 409-413.
[61] *Works*, I, 462-463.
[62] See his tract, "A Prophecy Concerning the Future State of Several Nations," *Works*, IV, 231-238.

Whatever in his reading he found unusual, his mind went out to meet like metal to Gilbert's magnet. And there were certain kinds of the unusual which he found so congenial to his nature that he seems never to have passed over an allusion to them. One of these is Africa, notably Egypt, the country that held for him the fascination of the serpent. There was something about the land of Osiris that appealed intimately to him: its great antiquity; the pyramids smelling of mystery and mortality; the strange and picturesque hieroglyphics[63] so provoking to a mystic; its

---

[63] Few subjects interested him more. Besides the complete chapter he has devoted to the "Hieroglyphical Pictures of the Egyptians" (*Works*, III, 148-152), there are references, among others, at II, 422, 427, 434, 437, 440, 452, 458, and 465. The books that Browne appears to have consulted most frequently were: Horapollo's *Hieroglyphics* (written originally in Egyptian at the beginning of the fifth century and translated into Greek, probably a century or two later); J. Pierius' *Hieroglyphica sive de sacris Aegyptiorum literis commentarii* (Basel, 1556); and Athanasius Kircher's *Oedipus Aegyptiacus. Hoc est universalis hieroglyphicae veterum doctrinae temporum iniuria abolitae instauratio* (Rome, 1652). (Gordon K. Chalmers emphasizes the first two; see his article "Hieroglyphs and Sir Thomas Browne," *Virginia Quarterly Review*, XI [1935], 554.) All of these contain illustrations that Browne carefully studied. Wilkin, in a long note, is at some pains to show that most of the lore thus taken over was by later standards erroneous. *Works*, II, 415, n. 1.

From Horapollo he seems to have lifted the following: "A custom there is in some parts of Europe to adorn aqueducts, spouts and cisterns with lions' heads; which though no illaudable ornament, is of an Egyptian genealogy, who practised the same under a symbolical illation. For because, the sun being in Leo, the flood of Nilus was at the full, and water became conveyed into every part, they made the spouts of their aqueducts through the head of a lion." *Works*, III, 168. Cf.: "And they depict a lion [for the rising of the Nile] because when the sun is in Leo it augments the rising of the Nile so that oftentimes while the sun remains in that sign of the zodiac, half of the new water is supplied; and hence it is, that those who anciently presided over the sacred works, have made the spouts and passages of the sacred fountains in the form of lions." *The Hieroglyphics of Horapollo Nilous*, trans. Alexander T. Cory (London, 1840), p. 42.

Again, cf.: "...the Egyptians hereby [by the figure of a basilisk] implied eternity, and the awful power of the supreme deity; and therefore described a crowned asp or basilisk upon the heads of their gods..." (*Works*, II, 422) with: "When they would represent Eternity differently, they delineate a serpent with its tail covered by the rest of its body: the Egyptians call this Ouraius, which in the Greek language signifies Basilisk: And they place golden figures of it round the Gods ... Inasmuch as it thus appears to have power over life and death, they place it upon the head of the Gods" (*Hieroglyphics*, pp. 5-6).

Compare also: "A woman that hath but one child, they express by a lioness; for that conceiveth but once" (*Works*, III, 151) with: "When they

millenaries-old mummies[64] "which Cambyses or time hath spared"; Old Father Nilus shrouding his head traditionally in the clouds on the Mountains of the Moon for the Middle Ages to speculate about—here surely, for a man of his temper, was God's plenty. What symbol of a nation's history could conceivably have appealed more to the mind of Sir Thomas Browne than the Sphinx!

---

would symbolise a woman that has brought forth once, they depict a Lioness; for she never conceives twice" (*Hieroglyphics*, p. 136).

Besides using such standard books on the subject, Browne picked up stray allusions from others. Cf.: "Hee [Wansleben] speakes of the hieroglyphicall cave in Upper Aegypt, the walls whereof full of hieroglyphicall and other old writing, butt much defaced,..." (*Works*, I, 222) with: "The only thing that pleas'd me among these Caves, was a Monastery, with a Church, all cut in a firm Rock.... The Walls were painted in an antick fashion, with the Histories of the New Testament, with Images of Heremites, and Saints, whose names were written underneath in Coptick Letters" (Johann Michael Wansleben, *The Present State of Egypt* [London, 1678], p. 231).

From Vincent le Blanc he takes a detail that is perfectly incidental and that has no marginal notice to advertise its existence. Browne has recorded it in that snapper-up of unconsidered trifles, the *"Musaeum Clausum"*: "Stones of strange and illegible inscriptions, found about the great ruins which Vincent le Blanc describeth about Cephala in Africa, where he opinioned that the Hebrews raised some buildings of old, and that Solomon brought from thereabout a good part of his gold." *Works*, IV, 247-248. With this, cf.: "In like manner we finde there Remainders of walls of above twenty five handfulls thick, with certain hieroglyphick characters engraved, not to be read, as the like is observed in Persia among the ruines of the town Persepolis. Many do conceive 'twas from hence Salomon fetcht his gold, as I said elsewhere; and these great ruines to have been of that Ages building, and by the same King." *The World Surveyed or the Famous Voyages and Travailes of Vincent le Blanc* (London, 1660), pp. 194-195. The earlier passage to which Le Blanc refers is as follows: "Some say this country in times past depended upon Ethiopia, and 'twas hither Salomon sent his Fleets for gold.... Though to speak truth, 'tis more likelihood Salomon fetched his gold from the mines of Sefala, which are not farre thence." *Ibid.*, p. 192.

Even the famous image of the snake with its tail disappearing into its own mouth is doubtless derived from hieroglyphics. Cf.: "...that the first day should make the last, that the tail of the snake should return into its mouth precisely at that time, and they should wind up upon the day of their nativity,..." (*Works*, IV, 41) with: "As by a serpent with the taile in his mouth, the revolution of the yeare" (John Greaves, *Pyramidographia* [London, 1646], pp. 50-51).

[64] When a friend of Wilkin, J. Crossley, wished to write something that he thought most likely to be accepted as Browne's, he wrote the spurious "Fragment on Mummies." *Works*, IV, 273-276. Aside from the fact that it

When we look among his works to see the result of this keen interest, we find them filled with allusions to books about his favorite country and continent. Leo Africanus' *History and Description of Africa*,[65] John Greaves's *Pyramidographia*,[66] and Prosper Alpinus' *De medicina Aegyptiorum*[67] are often laid

---

was, perhaps, the lowest literary trick ever perpetrated, the forgery is a brilliantly clever one.

Browne took much of his information about mummies from the book above mentioned, John Greaves's *Pyramidographia* (London, 1646). Cf.: "...the Egyptian embalmers imitated this texture, yet in their linen folds the same is still observable among their neatest mummies,..." (*Works*, III, 418) with: "...on the feet was a linnen cover (and so were all the scroles before mentioned of linnen)" (*Pyramidographia*, p. 50, n. e). Cf. also: "...the *Statuae Isiacae*, and little idols, found about the mummies, do make a decussation of Jacob's cross, with their arms..." (*Works*, III, 418) with Greaves's description of a woman's face in the bend at the coffin's top "with her arms expanded...by the signe of the crosse they did denote *spem venturae salutis*.... Of these crosses I have seen severall amongst their Hieroglyphicks; some painted, and some ingraven in this manner ✚ and some others amongst their mummies formed of stone (or baked earth) in this figure ⚏. At Rome on the statue of Osiris it is ingraven thus. **T**" (*Pyramidographia*, p. 51). Cf. also: "...the learned describer of the pyramids observeth, that the old Egyptians made coffins of this wood [sycamore], which he found yet fresh and undecayed among divers of their mummies" (*Works*, IV, 144) with: "...this coffine (if it be lawfull for me to conjecture after the revolution of three thousand yeares) I conceive to have been of sycamore...of which sort there are many found in the Mummies, very faire, intire, and free from corruption to this day" (*Pyramidographia*, p. 57).

Wansleben was also drawn upon. Cf.: "Hee went into divers caves of the mummies, and in one hee sayth hee found many sorts of birds, embalmed, and included in potts, one whereof hee sent into France. Hee also sayth, that he found empty eggs, whole and unbroaken, butt light and without anything in them" (*Works*, I, 222) with: "...in these [earthen] Pots were Embalmed Birds of all kinds ... And as I thought that the remembrance of a Custom so ancient, and superstitious, was worthy of our notice, I brought about half a dozen with me; some I have sent to the King's Library. We found also some Hens Eggs, empty, but entire without any ill smell or crack" (Johann Michael Wansleben, *The Present State of Egypt* [London, 1678], p. 89).

[65] Trans. John Pory, 3 vols. (Hakluyt Soc.; London, 1896). I shall refer both to that edition and to the Latin version, *Joannis Leonis Africani, Africae descriptio IX. lib. absoluta*, 2 pts. in 1 vol. (Leyden, 1632).
[66] London, 1646. Greaves was professor of astronomy at Oxford from 1643 to 1648.
[67] Paris, 1645. Alpinus was a Venetian physician and botanist, who held the chair of botany at Padua from 1593 to 1617. He spent three years in Egypt. His book, of 150 folios, is in the form of a dialogue between

under contribution; and, less often, such works as Duarte Lopes' *A Report of the Kingdom of Congo*,[68] Baptista Scortia's *De natura et incremento Nili*,[69] and Simocrates' *De Nilo*. J. M. Wansleben's *The Present State of Egypt*[70] and Hiob Ludolf's *A New History of Ethiopia*,[71] Browne appears to have bought as soon as they appeared,[72] the latter in the very year of his death. Furthermore, if we are to judge from the number of references to them, we can infer that the sections devoted to Egypt and Africa in such tomes as Giovanni Antonio Magini's geography,[73] Hondius' *Atlas*,[74] Strabo's *Geographia*,[75] Abraham Ortelius' *Theatrum orbis terrarum*,[76] Ptolemy,[77] George Sandys' *A Relation of a Journey*,[78] and Varthema's *Travels*[79] were well thumbed. It is especially significant that most of Browne's allus-

---

Alpinus and Melchior Guilandinus, who discuss first the general state of medicine in Egypt, then such matters as phlebotomy and scarifications. Browne also used another of Alpinus' books, *De balsamo dialogus* (Venice, 1591). Alpinus is said to be the first to have discussed the coffee plant in print.

[68] Translated by Abraham Hartwell from P. Pigafetta's selections in Italian (London, 1597).

[69] London, 1617.

[70] London, 1678.

[71] "Made English by J. P., Gent." (London, 1682).

[72] *Works*, I, 221-222 and 340.

[73] *Geographiae universae tum veteris, tum novae absolutissimum opus* (Cologne, 1597). The work contains first Magini's annotations on Ptolemy, Book I; then Ptolemy's eight books, followed by an index; then Ptolemy's maps and some more recent ones, with Magini's commentaries on the various countries.

[74] G. Mercator and J. Hondius, *Atlas; or, a Geographicke Description of the Regions, Countries and Kingdomes of the World*, 2 vols. (Amsterdam, 1636-38).

[75] *The Geography of Strabo*, trans. Hamilton and Falconer, 3 vols. (London, 1889-93).

[76] Antwerp, 1612.

[77] *Joannis Antonii Magini ... Geographiae, tum veteris, tum novae*, 2 pts. in 1 vol. (Arnheim, 1617). This was the edition in Browne's library. The first part is Ptolemy's geography, with some notes by Magini; the second part is Magini's. See *A Catalogue of the Libraries ...* (London, 1711), "Libri historici," Quart., 2.

[78] *A Relation of a Journey Begun An. Dom. 1610* (2nd ed.; London, 1621).

[79] *Itinerario di Ludovico de Varthema*, in *Scelta di curiosita letterarie inedite o rare*, No. 207 (Bologna, 1885). The work has been translated in Hakluyt Society publications as *The Travels of Ludovico di Varthema*, trans. John W. Jones, ed. George P. Badger (London, 1863).

ions to Belon's *Les Observations*[80] are to the second book, the one that has to do with Egypt.

A second interest that partially dictated his choice of reading was religion.[81] In his book *Science and Religion in Elizabethan England* (San Marino, Calif., 1953), Dr. Paul H. Kocher has made important contributions to the troublesome question of the relation between science and religion in the last half of the sixteenth century; his conclusions apply about as well to Browne's time. In general, he decides that, except for miracles, there was a tacit gentlemen's agreement not to trespass on the other's domain. As for the particular books on religion to which Browne gave his attention, we may notice first Duarte Lopes' *A Report of the Kingdom of Congo*, mentioned just above, which we know he read in Abraham Hartwell's translation. Hartwell dedicates his edition of this work (the second book of which is devoted to the natives' conversion) to the Archbishop of Canterbury and, in his "Epistle Dedicatory," he says that "it pleased God to draw them [the people of Congo] from Paganisme to Christianity,"[82] and he expresses the hope that the work will inspire his countrymen to evangelistic efforts elsewhere. Browne himself reveals similar concern over "the late conversion of the wild Americans."[83] Furthermore, one of the four books of Hiob Ludolf's *A New History of Ethiopia*,[84] which we know he read, is given over to "Their Ecclesiastical Affairs," principally their acceptance of the Christian religion. There were, then, reasons besides his preoccupation with Egypt why Browne should have enjoyed these two books. Du Loir likewise has passages that took his attention because of their religious burden,[85]

---

[80] Pierre Belon, *Les Observations de plusieurs singularitez et choses memorables, trouvées en Grece, Asie, Judée, Egypte, Arabie, et autres pays estranges* (Paris, 1553). See Berna Moran, "Sir Thomas Browne's Reading on the Turks," *Notes and Queries*, CXCVII (1952), 380-382, 403-406.

[81] One study of this side of Browne has been made by W. P. Dunn in *Sir Thomas Browne, A Study in Religious Philosophy* (2nd ed.; Minneapolis, 1950). See also Jeremiah S. Finch, *Sir Thomas Browne: A Doctor's Life of Science and Faith* (New York, 1950) and E. S. Merton, *Science and Imagination in Sir Thomas Browne* (New York, 1949), especially pp. 86-102.

[82] Page 2.

[83] *Works*, IV, 394.

[84] London, 1682.

[85] *Les voyages du sieur Du Loir* (Paris, 1654). This book, in the form of

as did Luis de Urreta's *Historia de la Sagrada Orden de Predica-dores, en los remotos reynos de la Etiopia.*[86] Sir Thomas' treatment of an incidental piece out of Pierre Belon will perhaps reveal most clearly his tendency never to lose sight of religion. In his tract "Of Troas," Browne has been distinguishing from the old Troy,

another maritime Troy, . . . which was this of St. Paul, and whereunto are appliable the particular accounts of Bellonius, when, not an hundred years ago, he described the ruins of Troy . . . and where, upon nearer view, he observed some signs and impressions of his conversion in the ruins of churches, crosses, and inscriptions upon stones.[87]

Actually, the sum and substance of what Belon has committed himself to was this:

L on veoit encore les ruines des eglises qui furent basties du temps que les Chrestiens y habiterent . . . et entre elles on veoit des croix entaillées dedens les pierres de marbre.[88]

And over the page he speaks of "un pilier de marbre blanc . . . qui avoit ceste inscription."[89] As will be noticed, he says absolutely

---

letters addressed to various people, recounts Du Loir's experiences in Smyrna, Constantinople, Greece, and Italy, a large part being devoted to the Turks and their customs. The religious ceremonies of the Turks are described in great detail, and near the end Du Loir says: "Celuy qui presche prend pour texte quelque verset de l'Alcoran, et je vous asseure que les plus devots Chrestiens pourroient profiter de la Morale de son Sermon." P. 153. This alone would have been enough to have fixed Browne's interest. He translated a Turkish hymn out of Du Loir's French and sent it to a friend with this explanation: "After the sermon ended, which was made upon a verse in the Alcoran containing much morality, the Dervises in a gallery apart sung this hymn, accompanied with instrumental music, which so affected the ears of Monsieur du Loir, that he would not omit to set it down, together with the musical notes . . . " *Works*, IV, 192. Du Loir's version was as follows: "La Predication estant finie, les Chanters [just previously he had called them "Dervichs"] qui sont dans une galerie, . . . accordant leurs voix avec des fluttes, qui pour estre merveilleusement harmonieuses sont deffenduës à tout autre sorte d'usage, commencent un Hymne à la cadance d'un tambour de biscaye." *Les voyages*, p. 153. The hymn, together with the musical notes, is given on pp. 154-155.

[86] Valencia, 1611. Urreta's *Historia eclesiastica . . . de los grandes y remotos reynos de la Etiopia* had been published at Valencia the previous year. Browne nowhere specifically mentions it, but it appears in *A Catalogue of the Libraries* . . . (London, 1711), p. 42, No. 2, and is distinctly the kind of book that Edward would not have added to the collection.

[87] *Works*, IV, 220.

[88] Pierre Belon, *Les Observations* (Paris, 1553), fol. 83.

[89] *Ibid.*, fol. 83 verso.

nothing about St. Paul and his conversion. If we reread the passage very carefully, we find that it does not necessarily say that he did, though nine out of ten readers would interpret it that way. Now, reading the words in the light of their source, we get this paraphrase: "Bellonius, sojourning in Troy, observed the ruins of churches in which I [Browne] can discern signs of St. Paul's conversion." It may be noted, in passing, that the inscriptions referred to by Browne concerned Roman emperors and had not the remotest connection with religion.

We have discussed only two of Sir Thomas' chief interests, in an attempt to show how such interests regulated his choice of books. Except for these two and a very few others that will emerge in the course of this study, the evidence is apt to be negative. Browne read in a somewhat informal manner. He was, as we shall see, looking for information on fairly defined subjects, but he looked for it in books of widely different natures. He sometimes let his mind dwell on the fables of Antiquity and the Middle Ages. Legend and truth have ever since made strange bedfellows in his works just because Pliny and Aristotle rested cheek by jowl on his shelves, as companionably as you please. This is not, of course, uttered in criticism; Sir Thomas was quite capable of rating the fables at their worth. Perhaps his whole attitude may be construed as the result of his desire to keep an open mind. Even that archfabricator Sir John Mandeville gets a hearing: "All which may still be received in some acceptions of morality, and to a pregnant invention may afford commendable mythology; but in a natural and proper exposition, it containeth impossibilities, and things inconsistent with truth."[90] Similarly, Pliny's *Natural History*,[91] though "there is scarce a popular error passant in our days, which is not either directly expressed or deductively contained in this work,"[92] receives much of his attention, not always for the purpose of refutation.[93] And, though, as a rule, he follows Aristotle in rejecting Ctesias and Herod-

[90] *Works*, II, 236.
[91] *Naturall Historie or The Historie of the World*, trans. Philemon Holland, 2 vols. in one (London, 1601). I shall refer also to the Latin version, *Historia mundi naturalis*, 3 vols. in one (Frankfurt, 1582).
[92] *Works*, II, 238.
[93] Cf.: "That the Ethiopians . . . did commonly eat them [locusts], is testified by Diodorus . . . and Pliny." *Works*, III, 320.

otus,[94] he is quite capable of adducing the latter when it suits him.[95] The Stagirite himself is, to a great extent, still a Bible to him, as perhaps he should have been; certainly Browne was not one to follow the Cartesian extremists and the Royal Society in their rejection of Aristotle and his work as pioneer.

As a general thing, then, it will not be possible to say he read this book or that with a preconceived purpose. Rather he was an adventurer in books, prepared to discover any point of special interest, though his eye learned early the habit of lighting on the particular subjects that were his favorites. This tendency meant, of course, that he would be apt to choose, for his library, books whose titles gave the best promise for an adventurer; it accounts for the presence there of such authors as Pliny and Solinus and Diodorus the Sicilian. One of the works he most frequently alluded to was Pierre Belon's *Les Observations de plusieurs singularitez et choses memorables, trouvées en Grece, Asie, Judée, Egypte, Arabie, et autres pays estranges.*[96]

His allusions, it should be carefully noted, are not to the great standard collections of voyages such as those of Richard Hakluyt and Samuel Purchas,[97] but to the lesser known travel books such

---

[94] *Works*, II, 235: "Aristotle . . . gives him [Ctesias] the lie no less than twice concerning the seed of elephants." Also, *Works*, III, 274: ". . . although we conceive this blackness to be seminal, yet are we not of Herodotus' conceit, that their [Negroes'] seed is black." Cf. *Works of Aristotle*, trans. Thomas Taylor, 9 vols. (London, 1812), VIII, 300: "For Ctesias the Cnidian is evidently wrong in what he says about the seed of elephants. . . . For the assertion of Herodotus is not true, that the genital seed of the Ethiopians is black." Aristotle has another allusion at VI, 105: "The assertion, therefore, of Herodotus is false, that the Ethiopians emit black seed." Browne (*Works*, II, 235) also quotes Strabo's rejection of Ctesias and Herodotus. Cf. *The Geography of Strabo*, trans. Hamilton and Falconer, 3 vols. (London, 1889-93), II, 241.

[95] *Works*, III, 188. Here he speaks of Egypt's having been built up from materials deposited by the Nile "according as is expressed by Strabo, and more at large by Herodotus, both from the Egyptian tradition and probable inducements from reason."

[96] Paris, 1553. Another was Johann Michael Wansleben's *The Present State of Egypt* (London, 1678; in Italian, Paris, 1671), whereof the subtitle is, "Wherein you have an exact and true Account of many Rare and Wonderful Particulars of that Ancient Kingdom." Cf. also C. J. Solinus' *Polyhistor, vel, rerum toto orbe memorabilium thesaurus* (Lyons, 1609).

[97] He alludes to Purchas only twice and to Hakluyt not at all. Neither collection is mentioned in *A Catalogue of the Libraries . . .* (London, 1711). He may have refrained from buying them because of the expense. He was

as those by Pierre Belon and Du Loir and N. C. Radzivill, preferably foreign. And it should be further noted that most of his information about foreign lands is drawn, not from travel books at all, but from works to which he may have gone in the first instance because of his scientific interests. I refer to such authors as Orta, Dioscorides, Hernandez, and Prosper Alpinus. Garcia da Orta's *Aromatum et simplicium aliquot medicamentorum apud Indos nascentium historia*[98] affords him data on such matters as the capture by the King of Siam of four thousand elephants[99] and elephants and swine living promiscuously in the Malabar woods.[100] From Dioscorides' *De medica materia*[101] he lifts a detail about incombustible cloth that has nothing whatever to do with medicine. In the 950 pages of Francisco Hernandez' *Rerum medicarum Novae Hispaniae thesaurus*[102] he finds the name of a double-headed monster, the *"amphisbaena europaea."* And Prosper Alpinus' *De medicina Aegyptiorum*[103] gives him data about the rainfall in Egypt,[104] about corpulence,[105] about the quality of the Nile's water.[106]

---

forever complaining about the costliness of books—and forever buying them. He owned four volumes of Moses Pit's *New English Atlas* (Oxford, 1680-82), one of the most expensive books of the time.

[98] Antwerp, 1567. Garcia, a sixteenth-century Portuguese physician and botanist, was for more than thirty years doctor to the viceroy of the Indies at Goa. His general method in the book is to give short descriptions of various drugs, and then the opinions about them of famous writers such as Avicenna, Dioscorides, Pliny. As Malcolm Letts conjectures, "Sir Thomas Browne and His Books," *Notes and Queries*, 11th Ser., vol. X (1914), 343, Browne may have read Garcia in "the abridged translation in the 'Exotica' of Clusius [Charles de L'Écluse], 1605." Letts's statement that he "had hoped to be able to show that he was familiar with this work in the original" is incomprehensible because there were numerous translations of the Garcia work in Latin from 1567 to 1605. There was also a French translation, *Histoire des Drogues*, trans. Antoine Colin (2nd ed.; Lyons, 1619).

[99] Cf. *Works*, III, 224-225 and *Aromatum*, p. 68.

[100] Cf. *Works*, II, 392-393 and *Aromatum*, p. 70.

[101] *De medica materia libri sex* (Paris, 1537). Cf. *Works*, II, 455.

[102] *Rerum medicarum Novae Hispaniae thesaurus, seu plantarum, animalium, mineralium Mexicanorum historia, ex Francisci Hernandez, novi orbis medici primarii relationibus* (Rome, 1649). On p. 797 there appears a picture representing a two-headed monster. Browne's reference is at *Works*, II, 458.

[103] Paris, 1645.

[104] Cf. *Works*, III, 256-257 and *De medicina*, fol. 11 verso.

[105] Cf. *Works*, IV, 131 and *De medicina*, fol. 14 verso.

[106] Cf. *Works*, IV, 131 and *De medicina*, fol. 16.

This interest in the impressive detail can easily be extended to the rest of his reading. In Aristotle he finds that the Syrian sheep were provided with tails "a cubit broad" and "so they are still, as Bellonius[107] hath delivered."[108] The detail is taken from the *History of Animals* and, significantly, from a chapter where Aristotle is discussing exceptional ones. In reading Leo Africanus, Browne is similarly interested in the enormous weight of an African wether's tail, a weight said to exceed one hundred pounds.[109] Leo says:

In Egypt there are divers that feede them fatte with bran and barly, untill their tailes growe so bigge that they cannot remoove themselves from place to place: insomuch that those which take charge of them are faine to binde little carts under their tailes, to the end they may have strength to walke.[110]

From Jan van Linschoten he takes that rarity of nature, the vegetable horn;[111] from Kircher's *China illustrata*[112] he chooses[113] a plant described by the author as "in provincia Leutung tota China celeberrima, et summe pretiosa." Du Loir yields him the

---

[107] Pierre Belon, *Les Observations* (Paris, 1553), fol. 150: "Les moutons de Syrie n'ont pas la queue si longue que ceux d'Egypte, mais ilz l'ont bien aussi grosse et large."

[108] *Works*, IV, 168. Cf. *Works of Aristotle*, trans. Thomas Taylor, 9 vols. (London, 1812), VI, 335: "In Syria, also, the sheep have tails a cubit in breadth."

[109] *Works*, III, 367: " . . . the tail of an African wether out-weigheth the body of a good calf, that is, an hundred pounds, according unto Leo Africanus . . . " Cf. Leo Africanus, *History and Description of Africa*, trans. John Pory, 3 vols. (Hakluyt Soc.; London, 1896), III, 945: "I my selfe sawe . . . one of the saide rams tailes that weighed fower-score pounds, and others affirmed that they had seene one of those tailes of an hundred and fiftie pounds weight."

[110] *Ibid.*

[111] " . . . Voyage to Goa, and Observations of the East Indies," printed in *Purchas His Pilgrimes*, 20 vols. (Glasgow, 1905-07), X, chap. 8, pp. 222-318. See p. 310, and cf. *Works*, IV, 249. It is of interest to observe that the Royal Society was not above inquiring into this phenomenon. Cf. Thomas Sprat's *History of the Royal Society* (London, 1667), p. 161: "What ground there may be for that Relation, concerning Horns taking root, and growing about Goa?" The Society got the answer it deserved.

[112] Athanasius Kircher, *China monumentis, qua sacris, qua profanis . . . illustrata* (Amsterdam, 1667), p. 178.

[113] *Works*, I, 236.

[114] *Les voyages du sieur Du Loir* (Paris, 1654), pp. 357-358. Browne has one allusion to the rare circumstance in his commonplace books (*Works*, IV, 395) and another in the "Letter to a Friend" (*Works*, IV, 44).

amazing statistic that, of the 7,000 inhabitants of Rovigno d'Istria, a third were maimed and halt.[114] Giovanni Botero's *Ragion di stato*[115] furnishes him with a detail about the Livonian Dvina's annual overflow.[116] And, finally, Joannes de Laet's *Novus orbis*[117] gives him the *"Phalangium monstrosum Brasilianum,"*[118] which De Laet characterizes as "genus non vulgare sed monstrosum." In other words, from a history of the New World, Browne picks out, from a section on Brasilia and a chapter on "Aliae Aliquot Plantae Brasilienses," an incidental detail about a rare spider. Besides this one, I have found no other reference to De Laet[119] in Browne's works.[120]

---

[115] *Della ragion di stato, libri dieci. Con tre libri delle cause della grandezza, e magnificenza delle città* (Ferrara, 1589). The book has been translated into English by Robert Peterson, *A Treatise Concerning the... Greatnes of Cities* (London, 1606).

[116] *Works*, III, 252.

[117] *Novus orbis, seu descriptionis Indiae occidentalis, libri XVIII* (Leyden, 1633), pp. 569-570.

[118] *Works*, III, 443.

[119] He did once scribble "J. de Laet" on the off page of his commonplace book. See British Museum MS. Sloan 1869, fol. 61 verso. This custom of jotting down his source was practiced by him all too infrequently.

[120] He would naturally be interested, among other notable things, in the unicorn. "Nor is it to be omitted, what hath been formerly suspected, but now confirmed by Olaus Wormius, and Thomas Bartholinus, and others, that those long horns, preserved as precious rarities in many places, are but the teeth of narwhals, to be found about Iceland, Greenland, and other northern regions, of many feet long, commonly wreathed, very deeply fastened in the upper jaw, and standing directly forward, graphically described in Bartholinus, according unto one sent from a bishop of Iceland, not separated from the crany." *Works*, II, 501. Cf. Thomas Bartholin's *De unicornu observationes novae* (Padua, 1645): "Animal Marinum circa Islandiam nostram, Groenlandiam, et reliquas Septentrioni viciniores Insulas frequens est et usitatum, nomine vulgari Narhval a cadaveribus quibus vesci solet appellatum Islandis, Balenae specie et magnitudine, quod anteriori dentium serie inter reliquos dentem effert eximiae quantitatis et vulgatis cornubus longitudine crassitieque parem Ingyros volvitur et striatos flexus ex majori radice ad extremum obliteratos." P. 95. And, again: "Restat ut dentati piscis porro hostorie insistamus cuius antea specimen accepimus Summi Wormii beneficio, cui deinde animalis istius ad balaenam propius accedentis figuram, sed rudiorem transmisit Episcopus Islandiae Borealis D. Thorlacus Scutonius, qui eum cum glacie Groenlandica eo appulsum vidit. Nos vero eius accuratiorem hic damus ideam non antea visam." P. 103. Underneath this passage there is a picture of a wreathed horn and, just below that, what looks like the same horn sticking directly forward out of a skull. The *De unicornu* is a book of 304 pages, divided into thirty-seven chapters, each treating an animal ordinarily considered to be *the*

Another noticeable point is that many of these interesting details are buried in their texts without any blare of trumpets in the shape of chapter headings or marginal fingerposts or indices to herald their existence. From a book on sacred and profane monuments, he borrows a rare plant;[121] and from a Turkish history he chooses such details as the width of the Nile[122] and the social status of Tamerlane's father.[123] Out of the very midst of some endless account, he ferrets some unobtrusive detail that yet has interested him. He seems, for example, never to have overlooked an allusion to the quandary that, according to tradition, sent the Stagirite to his watery death. Wherever mention was made of the tides of Euripus, no matter how incidentally, he must have made a record of it. One might, I suppose, expect to find such mention in Tommaso Porcacchi's *L'isole più famose del mondo*;[124] but how could one hope to find it in Mela's *De situ orbis* or Du Loir's *Voyages*? In a chapter entitled simply "Mediterranei Maris Insulae," Mela has these few words—nothing more: "Euripon vocant, rapidum mare, et alterno cursu septies die ac septies nocte fluctibus invicem versis, adeo immodice fluens, ut ventos etiam ac plena ventis navigia frustretur."[125] Sieur du Loir's experimental method[126] of disproving the same phenomenon must have appealed particularly to a man who

---

unicorn. This arrangement may have given Browne the idea, in his own chapter, "Of the Unicorn's Horn," of accepting many kinds of unicorn, instead of trying to determine on one. "...we are so far from denying there is any unicorn at all, that we affirm there are many kinds thereof." *Works*, II, 498. See also the significant notes on the unicorn in *The Works of Du Bartas*, ed. U. T. Holmes, Jr., J. C. Lyons, and R. W. Linker, 3 vols. (Chapel Hill, 1935-40), II, 387.

[121] See p. 124 *supra*.

[122] Richard Knolles, *Generall Historie of the Turkes* (3rd ed.; London, 1621), p. 549. Cf. pp. 135-136 *infra*.

[123] Knolles, *op. cit.*, p. 212. Cf. *Works*, III, 351.

[124] Venice, 1572, p. 35: "Negroponte Isola dell' Arcipelago è separata dalla Beotia da un lungo canale, che con un ponte la congiugne dalla parte di Ponente con terra ferma.... Il canale ha due volte il giorno tanto gran flusso d'acque impetuose, ch'è cosa mirabile." Cf. *Works*, Ill, 334: "Thomaso Porrchachi affirmeth in his description of famous islands, that twice a day it hath such an impetuous flood, as is not without wonder."

[125] Isaac Vossius, *Observationes ad Pomponium Melam De situ orbis* (The Hague, 1658), p. 43. Vossius reproduces the whole of Mela's work, and follows it with elaborate notes. Browne's reference to Mela is at *Works*, III, 334.

[126] Browne and Du Loir had much in common.

would hang out a kingfisher to learn which way the wind blew:[127]

Vous m'estimeriez bien peu curieux si je ne vous parlois point du flux et du reflux de l'Euripe, que beaucoup de personnes, et Mela[128] entre les autres, ont rapporté se faire sept fois le jour...je vous asseure que cette opinion est fausse....Je donnai un escu à un Battelier pour me mettre en un endroict ou je le pusse exactement voir durant un jour. Il ne se fait que quatre fois, de six heures en six heures comme à Venise, mais il est vray qu'il est si violent qu'il fait mouldre des Moulins de part et d'autre.[129]

Browne's allusion to gypsies,[130] taken from an incidental mention by Albert Krantz,[131] may be accounted for by his fairly active interest in nomads.[132] But no such explanation is forthcoming for a still more incidental reference to something by

---

[127] *Works*, II, 432.

[128] Knowing Browne's habits, we must always allow for the possibility that this mention of Mela by Du Loir was alone sufficient to have made Browne use him as additional authority.

[129] *Les Voyages du sieur Du Loir* (Paris, 1654), p. 301. Browne's version, drawn almost word for word from Du Loir, is as follows: "A later and experimental testimony is to be found in the travels of Monsieur Duloir; who about twenty years ago, remained sometime at Negroponte, or old Chalcis, and also passed and repassed this Euripus; who thus expresseth himself. 'I wonder much at the error concerning the flux and reflux of Euripus; and I assure you that opinion is false. I gave a boatman a crown, to set me in a convenient place, where for a whole day I might observe the same. It ebbeth and floweth by six hours, even as it doth at Venice, but the course thereof is vehement.'" *Works*, III, 335. In the same discussion, Browne speaks (p. 334) of Strabo's opinion on the subject. Cf. *The Geography of Strabo*, trans. Hamilton and Falconer, 3 vols. (London, 1889-93), II, 96. He also refers here to G. A. Magini and quotes from him, quite accurately. Cf. *Geographiae universae tum veteris, tum novae absolutissimum opus* (Cologne, 1597), fol. 176 verso.

[130] *Works*, III, 289.

[131] *Vandalia, sive historia de Vandalorum vera origine* (Cologne, 1518).

[132] He picked up the following information on the subject from Belon: "That they are no Egyptians, Bellonius maketh evident: who met great droves of Gypsies in Egypt, about Grand Cairo, Mataerea, and the villages on the banks of Nilus, who notwithstanding were accounted strangers unto that nation, and wanderers from foreign parts, even as they are esteemed with us." *Works*, III, 289. Cf.: "Estants entre la Materée et le Caire, nous en [Baumiens] trouvions de grandes compagnies, et aussi le long du Nil, en plusieurs villages d'Egypte....qui estoient aussi bien estrangers en ce pays la comme ilz sont aux nostres." Pierre Belon, *Les Observations* (Paris, 1553), fol. 113. And cf. also: "...Bellonius [deduces gypsies] no further than Wallachia and Bulgaria..." (*Works*, III, 289) with: "Et pource que leur origine est de Valachie, ilz sçavent parler plusieurs langues" (*Les Observations*, fol. 113).

Mela found in the latter's chapter, in *De situ orbis*, on Thrace. Edward had sent his father from London some of Isaac Vossius' observations on the geography of Mela, and, by a section of Mela thus delivered into his hands, Sir Thomas was set wondering about Mount Haemus and the "possibility of seeing the Euxine and Adriatick sea from the top thereof."[133] From the way Browne introduces it, one expects, when he goes to seek the passage in Mela's geography, to find that the detail has been emphasized there. But Mela, in the course of enumerating the mountains of Thrace, brings in the conjecture quite casually in two short lines and then immediately turns to a discussion of the people in the locality:

Montes interior attollit, Haemon et Rhodopen, et Orbelon, sacris Liberi patris, et coetu Maenadum, Orpheo primum initiante, celebratos. *Ex quibus Haemus in tantum altitudinis abit, ut Euxinum et Adriam ex summo vertice ostendat.* Una gens Thraces habitant, aliis aliisque praediti et nominibus et moribus.[134]

There are naturally abundant exceptions to this practice of selecting the incidental detail, or at least the kind of detail whose presence one would not normally expect from the book's title. If we find few allusions to matters related to his own profession, it is doubtless because Dr. Primrose's "learned discourse of Vulgar Errors in Physick"[135] had already covered that ground. We do get such allusions from time to time, but even those are apt to concern unusual cases. We surprise him, for example, speculating about the notable case, recorded in Knolles's Turkish history, of Duke John Ernestus Mansfield whose body "was opened, and not one drop of blood found, but his heart withered to the smallness of a nut."[136] And he is

---

133 *Works*, I, 220.
134 Isaac Vossius, *Observationes ad Pomponium Melam De situ orbis* (The Hague, 1658), p. 28. Italics mine. The passage is from Mela's own work. Vossius writes no note on it.
135 *Works*, II, 179. Dr. James Primrose published in 1638 his *De vulgi erroribus in medicina* (London), which was translated by Robert Wittie in 1651 under the title *Popular Errours. Or the Errours of the People in Physick* (London). There was also Laurent Joubert's *De vulgi erroribus medicinae* (Antwerp, 1600).
136 He notes this circumstance in his commonplace book (*Works*, IV, 423), and then returns to it in a "Letter to a Friend" (*Works*, IV, 41). The detail is found in Richard Knolles's *Generall Historie* (3rd ed.; London, 1621), pp. 1482-83.

similarly taken with Knolles's story of the Princess Coreski, who won her freedom from the Tartars by using "a precious stone of rare virtue, which applied unto the eyes of the brother of the Tartar, whose prisoner she was, in a short time recovered his sight."[137] From Minadoi's history of the Turkish-Persian wars[138] he learns "the exact method of flaying men alive," that is, "beginning between the shoulders."[139] This choice piece of horror must have been dispatched to Edward, for we find it being reproduced, in virtually those exact words, by the young Dr. Browne in one of his anatomical lectures before the College of Physicians in 1675.[140]

Other habits of Browne in reading and reproducing become just as clear. There is considerable evidence that he drew heavily on definitely circumscribed parts of books in a way that conveys the impression that he was reading those parts at the very

[137] *Works*, IV, 424. Cf. Knolles, *op. cit.*, pp. 1364-65.

[138] Giovanni Tommaso Minadoi, *The History of the Warres Betweene the Turkes and the Persians*, trans. Abraham Hartwell (London, 1595). The passage in Minadoi (p. 311) follows: "The miserable wretch [Macademo of Manogli] (having been too credulous) was stripped, and three great slashes made on his back, where they began to flea him. . . . And then the barbarous soldiers, pursuing their cruell action, made certaine other gashes upon his brest, and upon his stomake, and so drawing his skinne downeward, they could not bring it to his Navel, before he was dead, with most dolorous paines." The account is given quite incidentally, and Minadoi is not discussing methods of flaying in general but only this one particular case.

[139] *Works*, IV, 245.

[140] "To excoriate men alive is still a practise in Turkie and Persia, where they begin first to take of the skin at the back, and so proceede as Sigr. Tomaso Minadoi an Italian Physitian hath described it in his relation of the Persian warres. To flay men when they are dead is a custome in these parts." British Museum MS. Sloan 1914, fol. 8.

Sir Thomas was apparently in the habit of supplying Edward with ammunition for his lectures. He sent him, for example, elaborate notes on the ostrich (*Works*, IV, 337-339) with such paternal asides as, "Then you mention what you know more" (*Works*, IV, 339).

In a chapter of *Pseudodoxia*, Browne said about the same bird: "Leo Africanus, who lived in those countries wherein they most abound, speaketh diminutively, and but half way into this assertion, *Surdum ac simplex animal est, quicquid invenit, absque delectu, usque ad ferrum devorat . . .*" *Works*, II, 494. See Leo Africanus, *Joannis Leonis Africani, Africae descriptio IX. lib. absoluta*, 2 pts. in 1 vol. (Leyden, 1632), II, 766. Edward was, however, enough of a Baconian not to accept anything on authority. He fed an ostrich "a peece of iron which weighed two ounces and a half, which we found in the first stomack again not at all altered," and he seemed surprised that "ours died of a soden." *Works*, I, 329.

time of composition. All told, he alludes to Prosper Alpinus six times, twice within a page in his chapter "Of the River Nilus" in *Pseudodoxia* and the other four times in a single tract, "Observations upon Several Plants Mentioned in Scripture";[141] and it is further to be noted that he has taken all these allusions from five consecutive pages of Prosper Alpinus' book, *De medicina Aegyptiorum*.[142] References to Pierre Belon, on the other hand, are pretty well scattered through his works; but, to judge by those references, he was familiar mainly with the second book of *Les Observations*,[143] the book, significantly enough, that deals with Belon's voyage from Constantinople to Alexandria and lays particularly heavy stress on Egypt. Four of the six references to G. A. Magini[144] occur within three pages in the chapter on the Nile;[145] and the only allusions to Paul Rycaut[146] are in letters to Edward written within two months of each other.[147] With Du Loir it is the same story; though Browne again disperses the material, most of it is derived from the Frenchman's final letter, the tenth.[148]

This last example reveals another of Browne's habits; he shares with the ordinary mortal a noticeable familiarity with the beginnings and ends of books. I have found exactly one reference to Dionysius Periegetes;[149] this is to his description of the inhabited earth as resembling a sling; and that is taken from the first ten lines of his *De situ orbis*.[150] Browne's phraseology, when he goes about to localize the ark of Noah, is definitely borrowed from a section *heading* in Ralegh's *History of the World*.[151] The detail about the Princess Coreski,[152] men-

---

[141] *Works*, III, 256, 257; IV, 129, 131, 143, and 151.
[142] Paris, 1645, folios 11-16.
[143] Paris, 1553. Practically all the references are taken from folios 82-148.
[144] *Works*, III, 248 (twice), 249, 250, 274, 334.
[145] *Works*, III, 248-250.
[146] *Works*, I, 268, 272, 275, 276. The title of Rycaut's book is *The History of the Turkish Empire from the Year 1623 to the Year 1677.*
[147] Nov. 24, 1679—Jan. 19, 1680.
[148] See *Les voyages du sieur Du Loir* (Paris, 1654).
[149] *Works*, III, 290.
[150] Ferrara, 1512. The comparison occurs in line 7: "assimilis fundae."
[151] Cf.: "For on the mountains of Ararat, this is, part of the hill Taurus, between the East Indies and Scythia, as Sir W. Raleigh accounts it, the ark of Noah rested..." (*Works*, III, 244) and: "That the ark rested upon part

tioned above, is lifted from the conclusion of the life of Achmat in Richard Knolles' history.[153] From Prosper Alpinus' *De balsamo dialogus*,[154] he takes a bit from the last page;[155] while the devastating effects of the "poison of *nubia*"[156] are taken from the very end of Book VII of Leo Africanus' *History and Description of Africa*.[157] As for the extraordinary preponderance of lame inhabitants in Rovigno,[158] Du Loir mentions this on the last two pages of his last letter.[159]

At times Browne gives the impression that he is following the argument as set forth in *one* of his sources. In his chapter in *Pseudodoxia* on the Nile, he may well have borne in mind the general divisions of Baptista Scortia's book on that subject.[160] And a book like Duarte Lopes' *A Report of the Kingdom of Congo*[161] happened to contain within its 217 convenient pages just those things Browne was forever harping on.

But this was by no means his typical procedure. Two authori-

---

of the hill Taurus, or Caucasus, between the East Indies and Scythia" (*The Works of Sir Walter Raleigh*, 8 vols. [Oxford, 1829], II, 217).

[152] *Works*, IV, 424.

[153] *Generall Historie* (3rd ed.; London, 1621), pp. 1364-65.

[154] Venice, 1591, p. 26. This is the only allusion to that book I found in Browne.

[155] *Works*, IV, 151.

[156] *Works*, II, 528.

[157] Trans. John Pory, 3 vols. (Hakluyt Soc.; London, 1896), III, 836.

[158] *Works*, IV, 395.

[159] *Les voyages du sieur Du Loir* (Paris, 1654), pp. 357-358.

[160] *De natura et incremento Nili* (London, 1617). The book contains such chapter headings as "De Variis Nili nominibus," "De Nili Ostiis," "De Nili Origine," "De Nili Magnitudine," "De Tempore Incrementi Nili," and "An Incrementum Nili fiat ab eliquatis nivibus in Aethiopia?" These are just the matters discussed by Browne at *Works*, III, 246-259. Luis de Urreta's *Historia eclesiastica . . .* (Valencia, 1610) is a book of the same kind. In its chapter "Del Rio Nilo," there are such marginal notices as "Nombres de Nilo," "Corriente y discurso del Nilo," "Causas de las crecientes del Nilo," and "La Verdadera causa de la creciente del Nilo."

[161] Trans. Abraham Hartwell (London, 1597). The following descriptive sentences are reproduced from the title page of Lopes' book:

"2. That the blacke colour which is in the skinnes of the Ethiopians and Negroes etc. proceedeth not from the Sunne." Cf. *Works*, III, 263-287.

"3. And that the River Nilus springeth not out of the mountains of the Moone, as hath beene heretofore beleeved: Together with the true cause of the rising and increasing thereof." *Works*, III, 252-253.

Thomas Bartholin's book on the unicorn may have given him an idea for his general scheme of treatment of that subject. See note 120 *supra*.

ties please him better than one, three better than two; and, if he can get ten, he is like a child with new marbles. It is quite true that most of those ten may have been mentioned in his original source. But he goes glibly on to marshal them as if they had been his own recruits. As an example, we have the following discussion of how the Red Sea won its name:

> Sir Walter Raleigh, from his own and Portugal observations, doth place the redness of the sea in the reflection from red islands, and the redness of the earth at the bottom, wherein coral grows very plentifully, and from whence in great abundance it is transported into Europe. The observations of Alberquerque, and Stephanus de Gama, (as, from Johannes de Bairros, Fernandius de Cordova relateth) derive this redness from the colour of the sand and argillous earth at the bottom, for being a shallow sea, while it rolleth to and fro, there appeareth redness upon the water, which is most discernible in sunny and windy weather. But that this is no more than a seeming redness, he confirmeth by an experiment; for in the reddest part taking up a vessel of water, it differed not from the complexion of other seas. Nor is this colour discoverable in every place of that sea, for as he also observed, in some places it is very green, in others white and yellow, according to the colour of the earth or sand at the bottom. And so may Philostratus be made out, when he saith, this sea is blue; or Bellonius denying this redness, because he beheld not that colour about Suez . . . [162]

This is an imposing list of authorities. But their impressiveness is only apparent since most of them are taken straight out of the first-mentioned source, Ralegh.[163] The following are some pertinent extracts from a longish passage in his *History of the World*:

> As Philostratus in his third book noteth, and ourselves know by experience, it is of a bluish colour, as other seas are.[164]
>
> It seemeth to me by the view of a discovery of that sea in the year 1544, performed by Stephen Gama, viceroy of the East India for the king of Portugal, that this Sea was so called from a reflection of redness, both from the banks, clifts, and sands of many islands, and part of the continent bordering it.[165]

Ralegh then goes on to quote Castro, "a principal commander under Gama," who confirms the above-mentioned theory by

---

[162] *Works*, III, 261.
[163] He has done the same with G. A. Magini. Cf. pp. 153-154 *infra*.
[164] *The Works of Sir Walter Raleigh*, 8 vols. (Oxford, 1829), III, 82.
[165] *Ibid.*, p. 83.

alluding to the "red earth, or stone, which by reflection of the sunbeams, give a kind of reddish lustre to the waters." Then:

. . . those Portugals report, and we know it by many testimonies, that there are found in the bottom of this sea, towards the shore, great abundance of red stones, on which the greatest store of coral grows, which is carried into most parts of Europe, and elsewhere.[166]

These selections suffice to illustrate how Browne has gradually been filling in his picture from material furnished him by Ralegh. Of the six authorities mentioned besides Ralegh, three, Philostratus, Stephanus de Gama, and João de Barros, are to be found in Ralegh's *History of the World*. But Browne's picture is by no means finished; there are details unaccounted for. The allusion to Pierre Belon is easily explicable because Sir Thomas was perfectly familiar with his book[167] and was constantly introducing him as a reliable eyewitness. But there remains unexplained the mysterious "he" referred to by Browne who took up a vessel of water and who found that "in some places it [the color of the sea] is very green, in others white and yellow, according to the colour of the earth or sand at the bottom." The answer to this mystery must be sought among that rather bewildering fraternity of Portuguese and Spanish gentlemen whose names Browne sprinkles so prodigally through his paragraph. I refer to Alberquerque, Stephanus de Gama, João de Barros, and Fernandius de Cordova. The clue even to this secret is given by Ralegh, who, further on, alludes to "Johannes Barros, in his second decade, eighth book and first chapter."[168] And, when we come to consult the De Barros passage referred to, we find that Browne has examined either the original Portuguese or some pretty accurate redaction thereof:

Indo aquella Armada que Dom Estevam da Gama levava ao longo da costa da Abasia, . . . como era de navios de remos, que podiam correr per cima de muitos baixos, e restingas, que aquelle mar tem tanto, que elle D. João via agua chea de manchas vermelhas per muita distancia, e as vezes agua tão baixa que tocava o catur em terra, surgia logo, e mandava com baldes tomar

---

[166] *Ibid.*, p. 84.
[167] Cf. *Les Observations* (Paris, 1553), fol. 124 verso: "Quelques uns qui ont ouy parler de ceste mer, pensent que l'eau en est rouge, mais il n'en est rien."
[168] *The Works of Sir Walter Raleigh*, III, 84.

daquella agua, a qual vinda acima, via ser muito mais clara, e crystallina, que a do mar fóra des portas do estreito. Não contente com isto, mandava mergulhar alguns marinheiros, e traziam-lhes do lastro do chão huma materia vermelha á maneira de coral ao modo de ramos, e outras eram cubertas de huma lanugem alaranjada; e em outra parte onde o mar fazia manchas verdes, traziam-lhe outra especie de pedras assi em ramos, a que commummente lá chamam coral branco, com outra lanugem verde á maneira de limo, e onde a agua era branca traziam arêa mui alva. E não sómente nestes lugares baixos a superficie da agua em cima representava estas côres do lastro da terra, mas ainda em fundo de vinte braças por a agua ser mui pura, e crystallina.[169]

Here obviously are the details not found in Ralegh. Here is the "shallow sea," here the experiment of "taking up a vessel of water," here the various colors, green, and red, and white "according to the colour of the earth or sand at the bottom."[170] And the identity of that mysterious "he," who might have been any one of four gentlemen, is definitely fixed. Browne, basing his account squarely on Ralegh, has utilized one of Ralegh's own sources to amplify the latter's account. It was a practice he resorted to with fair frequency.

III

It becomes gradually evident through a study of this kind that Browne rested his work directly upon a system of commonplace books. No memory—not even Sir Thomas'—could have retained the vast storehouse of facts and opinions that is the *Pseudodoxia*. It would be of absorbing interest to have the notes he took over those forty-six long years of medical practice in Norwich, notes taken late at night while the quincunx of heaven ran low and during those all too rare vacations that he snatched from "the fruitless importunity of uroscopy."[171] Unfortunately, the most valuable documents have perished, and the score of volumes that have come to rest in the British Museum contain, for the most part, anatomical notes, Edward's

---

[169] *Da Asia de João de Barros e de Diogo de Couto*, 24 vols. (Lisbon, 1777-88), IV, 261.
[170] Browne may have confused *limo* ("mud" or "slime") with Spanish *limon* ("lemon") and so derived his "yellow." *Alaranjada* ("orange color") may also have suggested yellow to him.
[171] *Works*, II, 178.

letters, or tracts that have since been published by Wilkin and Keynes. There is left to us, however, an outline of Richard Knolles's *Generall Historie of the Turkes*[172] which, though it hardly affords us the data we might expect, must be closely studied.[173] Written in a fine, neat hand, it is an accurate, compendious digest of the chief events recorded in Part I of the history, with the corresponding page numbers in Knolles placed far out at the right edge of the manuscript. It reminds us of a schoolboy's painstaking outline of Burke's speech on conciliation; and, like that of a schoolboy, it trails off after the first zealous efforts. Only seven lines of notes are taken on the first fourteen pages of Knolles's Part II; on pages 266-272, only five lines. And then—he wrote no more. The chief events of Part I are, however, diligently summarized: the wrangling with the Persians, the wars against the Caliph of Babylon, Peter the Hermit's assertion of Christianity, Jerusalem delivered.

It will perhaps not seem remarkable, after the study we have been making, that Browne, in his published writings, should have used scarcely one fact from all these precious jottings. What he did use, and his manner of using it, is highly revelatory. " . . . we read, in the history of the Turks," he says in *Pseudodoxia*, "the Tartar horsemen of Selimus swam over the Nile from Cairo to meet the forces of Tonumbeus."[174] But he is concerned here solely with disproving that the Nile is *"totius Orbis maximus"* and is using the fact taken from Knolles only to show how narrow the river must be in some places. For that purpose he selects one detail from a fairly long account of a brisk skirmish between the Turkish Emperor and the Sultan of Egypt, the passage in question reading: "*Canoglis* also, the Tartar kings sonne and *Selymus* his brother in law, encouraging his horsemen to take the river, with losse of some few of his men recovered the further side, to the great admiration of the be-

---

[172] 3rd ed.; London, 1621.
[173] British Museum MS. Sloan 1910, folios 33-35. For other reading he did on Turkey, see Berna Moran, "Sir Thomas Browne's Reading on the Turks," *Notes and Queries*, CXCVII (1952), 380-382, 403-406. The author thinks Browne may have had in manuscript Robert Withers' "Traveller in the East. A Description of the Grand Signour's Seraglio" (published in London in 1650).
[174] *Works*, III, 250.

holders."[175] So far as the battle went, this notable venture was almost without significance, for the Tartars came in lamely after having been "carried away with the force of the streame" and rejoined their comrades rather ingloriously after the victory was won.[176] What in the long narrative seems to have stood out for Browne was, not the Tartars' bravery, but the narrowness of a river across which they and their horses could swim, a factor with which Knolles was wholly unconcerned. But the Nile was involved, and wherever Browne could pick up a new fact about that stream, he filed it away either in his memory, or, still more permanently, in one of those great commonplace books.

In a passage headed "Naval Fights,"[177] utilizing facts largely taken from Knolles,[178] he does show himself interested in military tactics, but here again for a special reason. The passage carefully analyzes the Battle of Lepanto, and seems to have been written expressly for the benefit of Tommy, Browne's younger son, who was in the Navy. In it he propounds several questions, asking, for example, if it was good tactics for Don John to have kept his reinforcements so long in reserve, and how Andreas Doria [Auria] could be justified in having absented himself from the fight. The questions are, in short, just the sort that a solicitous father might ask in order to teach his son the art of close reading and reasoning. In the course of them he makes a few mistakes himself. He asks, for instance, why Knolles "should not so much as mention... [the] commander" of the eight galleasses.[179] Actually, Knolles does mention him and there were six instead of eight galleasses.[180] But Knolles's account of the

---

[175] Knolles, *Generall Historie* (3rd ed.; London, 1621), p. 549.
[176] *Ibid.*, p. 550.
[177] *Works*, IV, 287-289.
[178] *Generall Historie* (3rd ed., London, 1621), pp. 873-887.
[179] *Works*, IV, 288.
[180] "The Christians had reposed great hope in six galeasses. . . . These galeasses conducted by *Franciscus Dodus,* a most expert captaine." *Generall Historie* (3rd ed.; London, 1621), p. 873. Browne may have been confused by Knolles's mention of "eight gallies of Sicilie" (*ibid.*). He makes other slips such as spelling "Auria" as "Doria." Caracoza, whom Knolles calls "a famous pyrat" (p. 875), is apparently elevated by Browne to a position in command of the Turkish fleet since Browne implies that he was to have given the orders for attack (p. 287). He was, indeed, "of great account

battle is long and these are trifling slips. Furthermore, Browne characteristically fills in details, which he thinks are missing from Knolles's history, from another book on the same subject, Peruzzi's *Famous Islands*.[181]

These two instances of Browne's use of material from Knolles's history are enough to indicate that he was not deeply impressed with the kind of thing with which the 1,511 great pages of that work are replete. Being a history of Turkey, the book is naturally full of tortures and bloody cruelties.[182] Per-

---

amongst the Turks," but his function in the battle, according to Knolles, was that of reconnoitering (p. 875). Sir Thomas makes other small changes that seem to indicate either that he was using notes contained in his commonplace books or that he was reviewing the Knolles account itself but hastily. He has Don John erecting Ali Bassa's bloody head "on the top of a pole" (p. 288), whereas it was "set upon the point of a speare" (p. 881). And he has John repulsed *thrice* before calling up his reinforcements (p. 288), whereas Knolles says merely, "the Spaniards attempting *sundrie times* to have entered the Turkes gallies" (p. 881).

[181] See Browne's own mention, *Works*, IV, 287. And for the manner in which Browne supplements from Peruzzi, see the following page.

[182] One picture of horror does seem to have impressed him. He records it in Tract XIII, headed "Musaeum Clausum...": "A noble picture of the famous duel between Paul Manessi and Caragusa the Turk, in the time of Amurath the Second; the Turkish army and that of Scanderbeg looking on; wherein Manessi slew the Turk, cut off his head, and carried away the spoils of his body." *Works*, IV, 247. Cf. Knolles: "*Caragusa* was by *Manessi*, at the first encounter stroke through the head and slaine. *Manessi* alighting, disarmed the dead bodie, and stroke off his head: and so loaded with the armour and head of the proud challenger, returned with victory to the armie." *Generall Historie* (3rd ed.; London, 1621), p. 312.

Browne's delight in conceiving scenes in pictures (it will be recalled that practically one whole book, the fifth, of *Pseudodoxia* is devoted to them) is connected with his fondness for poring over others' pictures. We have already seen how he probably examined with great care the hieroglyphical designs in such books as those of Pierius and Horapollo (see note 63 *supra*); and also how he studied the pictures of the "*amphisbaena europaea*" (see note 102) and of the unicorn (see note 120). When he alludes to the "metamorphosis of Ortelius" (*Works*, III, 479), he is referring to a design in one of Ortelius' maps. (The wrong one is given by Wilkin in his note to that passage. The reference is clearly to the inscription on the shield reading "metamorphosi." See Abraham Ortelius, *Theatrum orbis terrarum* [Antwerp, 1612], p. 107.) He instructs Edward to "learne the most authentic account how the half moone was set upon St. Stephen's; which, in Brawne's Booke of Citties, seemes a very noble one." *Works*, I, 168. He has been examining the splendid colored illustrations in Braun, particularly Map 21, in the sixth volume, of "Vienna Austriae." In that, the "Templum D. Stephani" is No. 1 on the chart and in the picture the church stands out prominently, with a good-sized ring decorating the top of the spire.

haps the secret of his not having used this material more exten-
sively is to be found in the question he posed[183] to Tommy:
" . . . whether it was handsomely done to cut off Ali Bassa, the
admiral's head, and fastening it on the top of a pole, to erect it
in his own galley?"[184]

G. Braun and F. Hohenberg, *Civitates orbis terrarum*, 6 vols. (Cologne,
1582-[1618]). The *"Phalangium monstrosum Brasilianum"* (*Works*, III,
443) he has seen represented in Joannes de Laet's *Novus orbis* . . . (Leyden,
1633), p. 570. In Hiob Ludolf's *A New History of Ethiopia* (London, 1682),
he is particularly interested in "some cutts . . . especially of some animals,
as apes, elephants, &c." *Works*, I, 340. And Jean Baptiste Tavernier has
made plain to him the Arabian coin "larin." Writing to Edward, Browne
says: "Tis the oddest shaped coyne that Tavernier hath in all his figures,
and better to bee taken in a good summe by wayght then tale, his figure
hath one foot a litle shorter then the other as yours hath." *Works*, I, 286.
It is quite true; in Tavernier's figure the lower prong of the queerly
bifurcated coin is shorter than the upper, but only very slightly. See *The
Six Voyages of John Baptista Tavernier* (London, 1678), Pt. 2, interleaf
between pp. 2-3.

[183] *Works*, IV, 288.

[184] Sir Thomas grew familiar also with the sequel to Knolles, Paul Rycaut's
History of the Turkish Empire from the Year 1623 to the Year 1677 (London, 1680). He wrote to Edward: "Your sister Betty hath read unto mee
Mr. Ricaut's historie of the three last Turkish emperours, Morat or
Amurah the Fourth, Ibrahim, and Mahomet the Fourth, and is a very good
historie, and a good addition unto Knolls his Turkish historie, which will
then make one of the best histories that wee have in English." *Works*, I,
272. Previously he had written of Rycaut's book: "In this are delivered the
taking of Newhewsell, the battail at St. Goddard, the fights between count
Souches and the visier of Buda, actions of Nicholas Serini, his burning the
bridge of Esseck, the Grand Signors being at Larissa, the seidge of Candia,
&c." *Works*, I, 268. Most of these references, it should be noted, are to
highly restricted parts of Rycaut's history, the part doubtless which the
filial Betty was reading to him in those late fall days when his own poor
eyes no longer served. Neuhäusel was "taken" on p. 142 of Rycaut's book;
the actions of Nicholas Serini, particularly the burning of the Esseg bridge,
are described on page 147, and Count Souches' skirmishes with Husaein
Pasha of Buda, on pages 162-164. One detail that stood out for Browne in
the siege of Candia was the grand seignior's absence from the post of duty,
"the Grand Signors being at Larissa." "During these Troubles," writes
Rycaut (p. 260), "the Grand Signor passed his time in hunting near Larissa," and twice more (pp. 241 and 254-255) he mentions the sojourn at Larissa. Browne's mention of the grand seignior's absence may have been his
way of protesting against cruelty, for the monarch drove his hunters, as he
had done in connection with Don John's exultantly waving the gory head
of Ali Bassa; or he may be implying contempt for a leader who is not in
the thick of it, as he did in the case of Andreas Auria. Sir Thomas takes
over the material quite accurately except for his usual orthographic liber-
ties. His "Newhewsell" regularly appears in the source as "Newhausel,"
and "Souches," as "Soise" or "Susa."

If, then, the notes on Knolles were typical, it would not matter so much that the rest have been lost. But there must have been a totally different kind of notes, those jotted down, often hastily, on pages that carried headings representing his favorite interests—such as Egyptian Hieroglyphics, Pictures, Negroes, Dead Sea, Nile, Elephants, Phoenix, Unicorns, and Mummies.[185] For such subjects he had the most extraordinary *flair*; he smelt them out from the remotest coverts. A system such as we have hypothesized meant that he would have, when he came to compose his most laborious and least inspired work, a vast collection of material ready for his artist's hand to mold. But it meant also that there would be severe limitations in that molding process. The lofty imagination with whose aerial flights we are so familiar in *Religio medici* and *Urn Burial* would be wing-clipped. The fact that it is accounts partially for that slight feeling of disappointment that we bring away from reading *Pseudodoxia*. By another author—by Bacon, by Burton—it might have been a great, or at least a greater work. With Browne, the close following of an outline and a great mass of factual data exercised a curbing restraint inimical to a nature such as his. He tries flight with the weight of authority dragging him to earth.

Though the system did, therefore, restrain his imagination, it gave him for the writing of *Pseudodoxia* a fund of information, in convenient compass, wherewith to combat the several vulgar errors. And in reproducing that information he shows often a scholar's accuracy. His quotations are so exact that we may assume either that he took the trouble to copy out into his commonplace books or that he set down precise references.[186]

---

[185] In a section of one commonplace book appear just such headings as we might expect Browne to have made (see British Museum MS. Sloan 1833, near the end). But unfortunately they are in Edward's handwriting.

[186] Examples are innumerable. Cf. George Sandys, *A Relation of a Journey* (2nd ed.; London, 1621), pp. 148-149, "They are generally fat, and ranke of the savours which attend upon sluttish corpulency," with Browne, *Works*, III, 41, where he reproduces word for word. The passage (*Works*, III, 128), "Of the vulgar ... three horses," is exactly quoted from *The Works of Sir Walter Raleigh*, 8 vols. (Oxford, 1829), IV, 456-457. Another Ralegh passage (*Works of Raleigh*, II, 221), "If the nations ... valley of Mesopotamia" is used verbatim (*Works*, III, 312). Cf. Sandys, *A Relation* ..., p. 94, "Two other branches there be that runne betweene these, but poore in waters," with *Works*, III, 248, " ... the other two ... [branches] do run between these, but poor in water." In this case Browne pretends

His scholar's conscience follows him also into his use of maps. He is perfectly accurate, for example, when he says that Abraham Ortelius shows eight mouths of the Nile in his "map of the Turkish empire" and eleven in "Egypt."[187] He is right also in making G. A. Magini show eleven.[188] When Edward is on his European travels, he does what any father might do, follows his son from town to town, his careful finger tracing the route. But he also does what perhaps few fathers would, indicates to him what mistakes he observes geographers to have made, and requests him to verify his corrections. "You may signifie how unsatisfactory you find the mappe either of [Ortelius] or others, in placing the towns through which you passed in Macedonia, as also in [Servia], omitting divers, and transplacing others."[189] In another letter he writes: "Most of the places [which Edward has mentioned in his letters] I find in my mappes, and Saal I thinck is Colonia Solunensis in Ortelius his mappe of Carinthia."[190] He inquires searchingly after Isaac Vossius, some of whose notes on Mela's geography Edward had sent him; asking with alert concern about Vossius' projected "mappe of Old Greece."[191] Seek him out at the prince's lodgings,

---

to be paraphrasing. Often, when he seems to be only paraphrasing, he falls into almost the precise phraseology of his source. Cf. Sandys, *A Relation* ..., p. 139, "Of those [ostriches] there are store in the desarts. They keepe in flocks, and oft affright the stranger passenger with their fearefull shreeches," with *Works*, I, 331, "There are great flocks of ostridges in the deserts, they keepe in flocks and often fright stranger passengers with their fearfull screeches." Cf. also Knolles, *Generall Historie* (3rd ed.; London, 1621), p. 886, "I thinke this present misfortune to bee rather imputed unto some fatall cause to us unknowne, than to the valour of the Christians," with *Works*, IV, 288, "...he told him the battle was not lost by the valour of the Christians, but by some fatal and unknown cause unto them." Finally, cf. *The Geography of Strabo*, trans. Hamilton and Falconer, 3 vols. (London, 1889-93), III, 231, "She also put an end to her life ... by the bite of an asp, or (for there are two accounts) by the application of a poisonous ointment," with *Works*, III, 126, "Strabo... hath also two opinions; that she died by the bite of an asp, or else a poisonous ointment." I suspect that these examples could be infinitely multiplied, that they are numerous enough to have a very considerable bearing on his famed style.

187 *Works*, III, 249. See Ortelius, *Theatrum orbis terrarum* (Antwerp, 1612), p. 113 (Turkey) and p. 115 (Egypt).

188 *Works*, III, 249. See *Geographiae universae tum veteris, tum novae absolutissimum opus* (Cologne, 1597), fol. 202 verso.

189 *Works*, I, 220.

190 *Works*, I, 187.

191 *Works*, I, 220.

he advises his son, and "ask his opinion of the mappe of Lauren-bergius, of Greece, which placeth the Pharsalian Fields on the north of the river Peneus; whereas at Larissa all accounted it to the south."[192] Here we have the spectacle of a father suggesting to his son that he should inquire from a noted foreign geographer as to the accuracy of a current map whose conclusions have been questioned in letters received by him from that same son!

With the Bible as well, he shows himself as familiar with maps as text, placing the tribes of Israel within their proper geo-graphical confines according to the lights of his day.[193] And, though he may make a trifling error in the dimensions of the Sea of Galilee,[194] that was his time's fault, not his. His habitual poring over maps is, furthermore, attested by the notes he scribbles into commonplace books; he wonders whether the defeated Mithridates, fleeing Pompey's legions, "went by the north of the Maeotis Palus, crossing the Tanais, or made a short cut, crossing the Bosphorus Cimmerius, and so marching through the Taurica Chersonesus, which is a much shorter cut."[195] And he wonders also, at great length and in detail, what route Hanni-bal took from Spain towards Italy.[196] He has been examining the records closely when he places Solomon's garden "on the east side of Jerusalem"[197] and when he finds that Sodom is customarily put too far from Segor, "which was seated under the mountains, near the side of the Lake."[198] And, when Tom sends back a description of his French travels, the teacher-parent readily identifies modern with ancient names: " ... the name of Santonna now Xaintes is in the geographie of Ptolemie who lived under Antoninus, as also Porto Santonicus where Rochell stands, and Promontorium Santonicum where now Bloys."[199] The accurate way in which he used Ptolemy's data

---

192 *Ibid.*
193 *Works*, III, 243. He shows similar acquaintance with the African tribes. See *Works*, III, 267.
194 *Works*, IV, 180.
195 *Works*, IV, 379. This is in Wilkin's section headed "Extracts from Common Place Books." The reference in the next note is to the same section.
196 *Works*, IV, 405-408.
197 *Works*, III, 429.
198 *Works*, III, 345.
199 *Works*, I, 7.

may readily be seen in the following passages, the first from *Pseudodoxia* and the second from Ptolemy's geography:

The place of his [Hippocrates'] nativity was Coos, an island in the Myrtoan sea, not far from Rhodes, described in maps by the name of Lango, and called by the Turks, who are masters thereof, Stancora, according unto Ptolemy, of northern latitude, 36 degrees.[200]

Cous, vel Cos, seu Coa insula est nobilissima 70. milliaribus in ambitu occupans . . . Nunc autem Lango, aut Negro, ac aliis placet, vocatur: sed Turcicè dicitur Stancora. . . . Urbem habet cum arce eiusdem nominis, quae à solis Turcis habitatur . . . Fuit autem Hippocratis Medicorum principis, patria.[201]

These ancient geographers[202] he used, of course, with proper discrimination, checking and rechecking Ptolemy and Mela, Herodotus and Eratosthenes; only his favorite Strabo, "that accurate geographer,"[203] seems to have escaped. In his exhaustive study of the Nile,[204] Browne is constantly correcting the old theories by appeal to fresh information. He finds that Old Father Nilus is by no means *totius Orbis maximus*.[205] And he can cite plenty of other rivers the world over that share the Nile's "unique" habit of annual overflow.[206] The tendency of scholars, interpreting too literally Browne's own statement that he was addressing himself only "unto the knowing and leading part of learning,[207] has been to underestimate his share in quashing effectively much misinformation about foreign countries that still passed current.[208]

---

[200] *Works*, III, 80.

[201] *Joannis Antonii Magini . . . Geographiae, tum veteris, tum novae* (Arnheim, 1617), fol. 214. In general, Browne used Ptolemy with great accuracy. He asks (*Works*, IV, 408): "How to salve that of Ptolemy who placeth the mouth of Rhenus in the latitude of 54, which is rather agreable unto the mouth of the river Elbe or Albis." Cf. Ptolemy, *op. cit.*, third map of Europe. The "Rhenus fl." is there represented as having three mouths into the "Mare Germanicum," and they pour in between lat. 53° and 54°.

[202] Browne was always quite ready to subject the Ancients to tests. "Having thus totally relinquished them in some things, it may not be presumptuous to examine them in others; but surely most unreasonable to adhere to them in all, as though they were infallible, or could not err in any." *Works*, II, 224.

[203] *Works*, III, 334.

[204] *Works*, III, 246-259.

[205] *Works*, III, 250.

[206] *Works*, III, 252.

[207] *Works*, II, 179.

[208] Although A. C. Howell is doubtless overstating the case when he says

While his system of recording data in commonplace books helped Browne, therefore, to collect a mountain of information, it also betrayed him into errors. Any study made here of the reverse side of his work, that is, of his *inaccurate* use of the sources, is made, not so much to reveal those inaccuracies, because most of them are inconsequential, as to find why he should have fallen into them. They concern us only to the extent of our asking: why he made a particular mistake; in how many cases the paternity was the wish; whether, because of his very strong prejudices, he unconsciously misrepresented; whether he occasionally descended to dishonesty (of however mild a sort); or whether the error was due to just sheer carelessness.

The first kind of mistake has to do with figures. Anyone who has agonized over Browne's scrawl can readily understand his misreading his own writing, particularly in the case of a figure hastily scribbled down. In one instance G. A. Magini had written quite clearly: "Maragnon quoque fluvius in immensam latitudinem ac longitudinem patescit; ferunt enim navigatum fuisse sex millibus milliaribus, ac eius ostium 70. leucas complecti."[209] Which Browne reproduces: "... the river Oregliana ... opens in a channels [*sic*] of *ninety* leagues broad."[210] A similar mistake in figures is made in citing facts from Leo Africanus, who had said of the city of Arzila:

À Mahumetanis verò anno Hegirae nonagesimo quarto capta fuit, qui per ducentos viginti annos urbem servarunt, donec Angli ingenti exercitu Gothorum persuasu obsidione civitatem cinxerunt.[211]

that "the *Vulgar Errors* was on every bookshelf and was a sort of *Popular Science* magazine of its day" ("Sir Thomas Browne and Seventeenth-Century Scientific Thought," *Studies in Philology*, XXII, 1925, 79), the extent of its influence has, without any question, been underestimated.

[209] *Geographiae universae tum veteris, tum novae absolutissimum opus* (Cologne, 1597), fol. 283. Another Latin edition (1608) also has "70. leucas." The Italian edition (Venice, 1598) has "settanta leuche" (fol. 205).

[210] *Works*, III, 250.

[211] *Joannis Leonis Africani, Africae descriptio IX. lib. absoluta*, 2 pts. in 1 vol. (Leyden, 1632), II, 403-404. In Pory's translation, "the Mahumetans wan it in the yeere of the Hegeira 94. and helde the same for two hundred and twenty yeeres, till such time as the English at the persuasion of the Goths besieged it with an huge armie.... The English having good successe tooke the citie, and so wasted it with fire and sword, that scarce one

Browne's version is:

A particular Narration of that famous Expedition of the English into Barbary, in the ninety-fourth year of the Hegira, so shortly touched by Leo Africanus, whither called by the Goths, they besieged, took and burnt the city of Arzilla possessed by the Mahometans . . .[212]

It is inconceivable that so good a Latin scholar as Sir Thomas, coming direct to the passage, should have made the mistake. But in the notes it is easy to see how the "94," Leo's date of the first siege by the Mahometans, should have got transferred to the second siege by the English, with the result that Browne has Arzila falling to his countrymen two centuries too early.

Another type of error is the exaggeration of statements, indulged in for various reasons. Such errors may be due to a strong original impression. In a letter to Edward of October 15, 1680, he recalls that, when he read Thomas Gage's book on travels in America "many yeares ago," he was much surprised to find that there were "twentie thousand coaches in Mexico."[213] What Gage had said was:

In my time it [the City of Mexico] was thought to be of between thirty and forty thousand inhabitants Spaniards, who are so proud and rich, that half the City was judged to keep Coaches, for it was a most credible report that in Mexico in my time there were above fifteen thousand Coaches.[214]

In a man naturally critical of travelers' stories, it is startling to find such credence, particularly since Gage has modified his assertion by "it was a most credible report." If Browne was simply remembering, as seems likely from the way his sentence is phrased, we can see how so impressive a figure as "above fifteen thousand" might easily slide over into "twentie thousand." That kind of unconscious exaggeration from original impression is being constantly indulged in by us all.

On the other hand, it is probable that we have examples of deliberate reduction of patent exaggerations appearing in his sources. Du Loir vouches for the astonishing fact that, of Rovigno's nine thousand inhabitants, seven thousand were lame!

---

citizen escaped." *History and Description of Africa*, trans. John Pory, 3 vols. (Hakluyt Soc.; London, 1896), II, 504-505.
[212] *Works*, IV, 241.
[213] *Works*, I, 288.
[214] Thomas Gage, *A New Survey of the West-Indies* (London, 1655), p. 56.

Je fus encor bien plus estonné quand plusieurs personnes dignes de foy m'asseurerent que de neuf mille habitans qui sont dans Rovigno il y en a sept mille de boiteux.[215]

Browne, scribbling that down into a commonplace book, makes the absurdity a little less absurd:

But how the people of Rovigno come to be lame, so that among seven thousand of that city, about a third part are lame, as Du Loir hath observed, is yet to be inquired.[216]

He seems to have jotted down a statement worth investigating, in which there must be some truth. But the margin of error is materially reduced in his allowance for travelers' lies. In another place he modifies a wild assertion of Leo's.

For if, as Leo Africanus reporteth, the tenth part of a grain of the poison of *nubia* will dispatch a man in two hours . . . we cannot as impossible reject this way of destruction . . .[217]

What had actually been said was:

Reperitur et hic venenum praesentissimum, cuius si granum unum inter decem homines fuerit divisum, ante quartam horae partem omnes necat: si verò uni detur, confestim eodemque instante interficit.[218]

In spite of Africa's age-old reputation as mother of monsters and purveyor of poisons, Browne hesitates to believe that any drug could act quite so disastrously.

There is still another kind of slip, due in this instance to over-eagerness, to a zealousness for clinching the point. Here he catches sight of an argument in his favor and he slightly stretches his opponent's words for emphasis. If this be dishonesty, make the most of it. As an instance, in his chapter with the bizarre and unlovely title, "That Jews Stink,"[219] he attributes to George

---

[215] *Les voyages du sieur Du Loir* (Paris, 1654), pp. 357-358.

[216] *Works*, IV, 395.

[217] *Works*, II, 528. See page 10 *supra*.

[218] *Joannis Leonis Africani, Africae descriptio IX. lib. absoluta*, 2 pts. in 1 vol. (Leyden, 1632), II, 661. Pory's version follows: "Heere is also a most strong and deadly poison, one graine whereof being divided amongst ten persons, will kill them all within lesse then a quarter of an hower: but if one man taketh a graine, he dieth thereof out of hand." *History and Description of Africa*, trans. John Pory, 3 vols. (Hakluyt Soc.; London, 1896), III, 836.

[219] *Works*, III, 36-43.

Sandys, in the heat of his argument, the extreme statement: "They [Jews as a people] are generally fat . . . and rank of the savours which attend upon sluttish corpulency."[220] Now Sandys may have thought so, but he at least has the moderation to restrict the charge to *some* Jewish *women*: "To speake a word or two of their women . . . They are generally fat, and ranke of the savours which attend upon sluttish corpulency."[221] Since Browne is here interested, as will be remembered, in disproving "that Jews stink," we have probably a case of reducing his opponent's contention to an absurdity by overstating it.

He has done the same thing with Strabo, who, he says, contends that "the Britons were so simple, that though they abounded in milk, they had not the artifice of cheese."[222] Actually, Strabo had alluded only to *some* Britons: "Quidam igitur lactis abundantes: conficiendi Casei: per imperitiam: prorsus sunt ignari."[223]

The current of his argument sweeps him away again when he is trying to establish the point that new Troy was close to the seaside:

. . . not an hundred years ago, he [Pierre Belon] described the ruins of Troy with their baths, aqueducts, walls, and towers, to be seen from the sea as he sailed between it and Tenedos; and where, upon nearer view, he observed some signs and impressions of his [St. Paul's] conversion in the ruins of churches, crosses, and inscriptions upon stones.[224]

Now, however he intended the passage to be interpreted, the

220 *Works*, III, 41.
221 *A Relation of a Journey* (2nd ed.; London, 1621), pp. 148-149.
222 *Works*, III, 245.
223 *Strabonis geographia* (no pagination; Rome, no date). This passage is in Bk. IV. In the English edition it is: "Some of them, though possessing plenty of milk, have not skill enough to make cheese." *The Geography of Strabo*, trans. Hamilton and Falconer, 3 vols. (London, 1889-93), I, 297. We have here another case of the *reductio ad absurdum* argument through exaggeration. The same kind of mistake is made in citing Prosper Alpinus. Browne speaks of "the present Egyptians, who are observed by Alpinus to be the fattest nation, and men to have breasts like women." *Works*, IV, 131. But Alpinus was talking about the people of Cairo: "Nusquam gentium memini me vidisse in tanto numero ita perpingues homines, quales Cayri observantur. Ex viris plurimos usque adeo pingues inspexi, ut mammas haberent longe mulierum maximis mammis maiores, crassiores, ac pinguiores." *De medicina Aegyptiorum* (Paris, 1645), fol. 14 verso.
224 *Works*, IV, 220.

modern reader certainly infers that, to substantiate his own argument, Browne is using a supposed statement by Belon that he had clearly seen from the sea certain evidence visible only at close range. But Belon unequivocally states that, though he could make out the outlines of the ruins from the sea, it was on another and a *land* journey that he was able to isolate the details:

Et pource que je les ay esté veoir *par terre*, j'en diray ce qu'on en veoit de reste: et suivant nostre navigation dirai aussi ce qu'on en veoit de la mer . . . Je fuz quatre heures à l'entourner, tant à pied qu'à cheval.[225]

Overzealousness, it seems, caused him to warp the truth in the foregoing instances. It is easy to explain away his misrepresentation of Varthema in his chapter "Of the Unicorn's Horn." He is laboring, for the moment, to set up the fact that no two writers agree about the animal itself. "Pliny affirmeth it is a fierce and terrible creature; Vartomannus, a tame and mansuete animal."[226] In the only section devoted to the unicorn that I have found in Varthema, the latter says, "Varamente questo mostra de essere un *ferocissimo*, et deserto animale."[227] It may be that Browne assumed the particular creature referred to by Varthema was tame because it was kept in the Temple of Mecca. Or, more likely still, he had written in his notes that the animal was there and neglected to mention its fierceness. There must have been among those same notes plenty of examples of writers who opposed Pliny's theories; he was simply unfortunate in having chosen the wrong entry. That his notes on the unicorn were in some confusion is indicated by the fact that elsewhere he fathers upon Varthema a description of that animal as having "the head of a deer and the tail of a boar."[228] Varthema does say, "ha la testa come un cervo";[229] but it is Pliny who speaks

---

[225] *Les Observations* (Paris, 1553), fol. 82 verso and fol. 83. Cf. pp. 120-121 *supra*.

[226] *Works*, II, 499.

[227] *Itinerario di Ludovico de Varthema*, in *Scelta di curiosita letterarie inedite o rare*, No. 207 (Bologna, 1885), p. 46. In *Works*, III, 146, Browne again refers to Varthema: "If it be made bisulcous or cloven-footed, it agreeth unto the description of Vertomannus." Cf. *Itinerario*, p. 46: "El pede suo è un poco fesso davanti."

[228] *Works*, III, 146.

[229] *Itinerario*, p. 46.

of its having the tail of a boar: "Capite cervo, pedibus elephanto, *cauda apro.*"[230]

And it is doubtless because of the confusion in his notes that he makes other similar small mistakes. In having Horapollo say that the vulture was a symbol of the male,[231] he causes him to deny conventional hieroglyphics;[232] he makes Herodotus say that King Necho himself circumnavigated Africa;[233] and has "that accurate geographer" Strabo saying almost the contrary of what he did say.[234] He makes Lopes say "*Spanish* plantations" whereas Lopes was actually speaking of the Portuguese.[235] In addition, he represents Garcia da Orta as signifying the King

---

[230] *Historia mundi naturalis*, 3 vols. in one (Frankfurt, 1582), I, 114.

[231] *Works*, III, 150: "We shall instance but in few, as they stand recorded by Orus. The male sex they expressed by a vulture, because of vultures all are females, and impregnated by the wind..."

[232] Cf. *The Hieroglyphics of Horapollo Nilous*, trans. Alexander T. Cory (London, 1840), p. 23: "They signify by it [a vulture] a mother, because in this race of creatures there is no male....the eggs of the vultures that are impregnated by the wind possess a vital principle." Cf. also J. Pierius, *Hieroglyphica sive de sacris Aegyptiorum literis commentarii* (Basel, 1556), fol. 131 verso. On this same page there is a picture headed, "Mater Sive Naturae Genius," which shows a face (intended to represent the wind) blowing on the tail of a vulture. See Kester Svendsen, *Milton and Science* (Cambridge, Mass., 1956), pp. 142-143.

[233] *Works*, IV, 418-419: "Yet Herodotus reports the same was done before; that Necho, King of Egypt, by the help of Phoenicians, sailed from the Red Sea, round about Africa, unto Cadiz." Cf. Herodotus' *History*, trans. G. C. Macaulay, 2 vols. (London, 1914), I, 307: "He [Necōs]...sent Phenicians with ships, bidding them sail and come back through the Pillars of Heracles to the Northern Sea and so to Egypt."

[234] *Works*, IV, 405: "...Strabo delivereth that Nismes exceeded Narbona in dominion but not in populosity . . ." Cf. *Strabonis geographia* (no pagination; Rome, no date), Bk. IV: "Arecomiscorum vero Metropolis Nemausus extat. Alienigena quidem plebe: et mercatorum numero: longe Narbone inferior. Ceterum regende civitatis forma: supior." The translation is to be found in *The Geography of Strabo*, trans. Hamilton and Falconer, 3 vols. (London, 1889-93), I, 278.

[235] *Works*, III, 266: "Edvardus Lopez testifieth of the Spanish plantations, that they retained their native complexions unto his days." Cf. Duarte Lopes, *A Report of the Kingdom of Congo*, trans. Abraham Hartwell (London, 1597), p. 19: "It is as certaine a thing as may be, that under the Equinoctiall, there are people which are borne almost all white, as... in the Isle of San Thomas which...was at the first inhabited by the Portingalles...and for the space of a hundred yeares and upwardes their children were continually white...And so likewise the children of the Portingals, which are borne of the women of Congo, do incline somewhat towards white."

of Siam instead of the King of Pegu[236]—misled here by a marginal note. And, finally, Strabo apparently ascribes to Aristobulus what was actually uttered by Onesicritus.[237]

There are but two more points to be made with regard to Browne's system; and they can be made quickly. The practice of listing data under a single head leads to trouble because, when the author comes to compose, he is sometimes undiscriminating in the way he lumps material. Let us say, for example, that Browne has a heading "Locusts." Under that he lists all the authors who have ever mentioned that locusts have served as human food. And you have as a result such an *omnium gatherum* as this: "That the Ethiopians, Mauritanians, and Arabians did commonly eat them, is testified by Diodorus, Strabo, Solinus, Aelian, and Pliny."[238] The fact is, of course, that no one of those men, whose names carry such weight, has mentioned that locusts were eaten by all those peoples.[239]

We can think of another possible kind of heading, "Strabo." Under that favorite name, Browne may have quoted much that

---

[236] *Works*, III, 224-225: "Garcias ab Horto . . . who relates that at one venation the King of Siam took four thousand [elephants]." Cf. Garcia da Orta, *Aromatum et simplicium aliquot medicamentorum apud Indos nascentium historia* (Antwerp, 1567), p. 68. There are three marginal notations, "Rex Sian," "Rex Pegu," and "Elephantorum Venatio." Browne did not notice that the monarch had changed by the time elephant hunting was introduced.

[237] *Works*, III, 264: The opinion that the sun caused the Negroes' blackness "was I perceive rejected by Aristobulus a very ancient geographer, as is discovered by Strabo." Cf. *The Geography of Strabo*, trans. Hamilton and Falconer, 3 vols. (London, 1889-93), III, 87. Browne was misled by Strabo's "the followers of Aristobulus." Among them was Onesicritus who took sharp issue with Theodectes, who believed in the theory.

[238] *Works*, III, 320.

[239] Examples of this tendency could be infinitely multiplied. Cf. *Works*, II, 511: " . . . as Solinus reports, the Arabians also and Indians [abstain from swine flesh]." C. J. Solinus, *Polyhistor, vel, rerum toto orbe memorabilium thesaurus* (Lyons, 1609), p. 148, makes the point about Arabians; but with Indians he is referring to all flesh (p. 183). The Nile, says Browne (*Works*, III, 250), is "called therefore *Fluviorum pater*, and *totius Orbis maximus*, by Ortelius." However, Ortelius uses the latter term—*Theatrum orbis terrarum* (Antwerp, 1612), p. 4—but not the former. Ole Worm is mentioned (*Works*, II, 501) as having said that many of the "unicorns' horns" were narwhales' teeth. But it is Bartholin, not Worm, who so characterizes them (see *De unicornu observationes novae*, Padua, 1645, p. 95). Worm makes no such assertion.

impressed him without troubling always to distinguish between what was the author's and what were merely his quotations. The result is that poor Strabo is made to stand, in Browne's own works, not only for statements which he did not utter but, occasionally, for statements with which he downright disagreed.

IV

Our particular approach in the preceding sections of this study has necessarily involved a scattering of the material. There has, in other words, been no opportunity thus far to follow Sir Thomas straight through a whole argument to determine his methods in the consecutive use of his sources. For this purpose, possibly the most typical example we could choose is his chapter in *Pseudodoxia* on the Nile.[240] His procedure here is essentially that of the scholar.

He starts with the general statement that many ideas currently accepted about the Nile are unfounded. And he formulates the chief fallacies in five main headings; namely, that the Nile has seven mouths, that it is the largest river in the world, that it alone inundates regularly and that its increase begins always on the same day, that it never rains in Egypt, and that several attempts have been made to cut a canal between the Mediterranean and the Red Sea. The chapter is conceived as a whole and planned with extraordinary care except for the conclusion which, as we shall presently see, is something of an afterthought. Browne resorts first to his customary procedure of examining the Ancients' testimony as refuted or corroborated by the Moderns, to citation from the Bible with an almost jaunty air of "that settles the matter,"[241] to commonsensical reasoning usually in the form of argument from analogy. His use of the sources is, in the main, admirably accurate. The conclusions he deduces from those sources are not always quite so admirable. He is himself subject at times to the "false Deduction," against which he warns others

---

[240] *Works*, III, 246-259.
[241] Cf. *Works*, II, 32: "They who, to salve this, would make the deluge particular, proceed upon a principle that I can no way grant; *not only upon the negative of Holy Scriptures*, but of mine own reason . . . " Italics mine.

in the preamble to his great tract,[242] just as he is sometimes subject to "obstinate Adherence unto Antiquity"[243] so long as Antiquity is spoken for by one of his favorites.

In proving that seven is not the number of the Nile's mouths, he calls forth the authority of seven Ancients: Homer, Eratosthenes, Aristotle, Herodotus, Strabo, Ptolemy, and Pliny. Of two of these, Herodotus and Pliny, he has spoken unfavorably elsewhere in his works. But they serve his purpose well enough here. Homer, he says, "hath given no number of its channels, nor so much as the name thereof in use with all historians."[244] It is well known that Homer customarily uses Αἴγυπτος.[245] Eratosthenes, Browne adds, "in his description of Egypt hath likewise passed them over."[246] And so he has, at least in the fragment of that author that Strabo has obligingly handed down to us.[247] Then we come to more substantial authority. Aristotle, in the first book of *Meteors*, Browne says, maintains that lower Egypt was "a mere gained ground" made "by the settling of mud and limous matter brought down by the river Nilus."[248] He then notes that Aristotle, resorting to Browne's own favorite argument from analogy, cites the case of Maeotis Palus, to which Browne adds the example of the River Gihon.[249] "All the mouths," said Aristotle, "of the Nile therefore, except one, the Canobic, appear to have been made by the hand, and not to have been formed by the river."[250] And later he says:

... the whole region of the Egyptians whom we assert to be the most ancient of men, appears to have been made, and to be the work of the river Nile. ... It is evident that from mud being collected pools and dry land are formed. ... The bottom also of the lake Maeotis has become ... much increased by the inundations of rivers.[251]

---

[242] *Works*, II, 202.
[243] *Works*, II, 214.
[244] *Works*, III, 246.
[245] Or he might, on occasion, use some such circumlocution as "Egypt's heaven-descended stream" (*Odyssey*, IV, 581).
[246] *Works*, III, 246.
[247] *The Geography of Strabo*, trans. Hamilton and Falconer, 3 vols. (London, 1889-93), III, 217 ff.
[248] *Works*, III, 246.
[249] *Works*, III, 246-247.
[250] *Works of Aristotle*, trans. Thomas Taylor, 9 vols. (London, 1812), V, 477.
[251] *Ibid.*, pp. 481-482.

Aristotle is arguing that it is absurd for people to maintain that the Egyptians are "the most ancient of men" since their country is comparatively new. Browne assumes that, since the country has been formed by the river's depositing of alluvial materials, there can be no set number of mouths to the Nile. He must have felt that one doubtful argument deserves another.

Sir Thomas has so far been building his argument by the increasing details of his authorities. Herodotus, he finds, "makes mention of seven, but carelessly of two hereof, that is, Bolbitinum and Bucolicum," for the reason that those two channels were artificial.[252] Says Herodotus: "Nam quae Bolbitinum et Boculicum nominantur, non sunt nativa ostia, sed effossa."[253] And now Browne plays his trump among the Ancients, calling forth "that accurate geographer Strabo" to settle the matter once and for all. The notable Strabo, he says, names but two mouths and "plainly affirmeth there were more than seven."[254] It is true the Greek had said:

Duo itaque sunt nili hostia: Alterum Pelusiacum: alterum canopicum et heracleoticum. Inter que alia. v. hostia sunt: mentione digna: alia vero tenuiora permulta. A primis enim partes quedam obrupte.[255]

But the part which Browne uses immediately thereafter and which he distinctly ascribes to so weighty an authority as Strabo is, as a fact, lifted direct out of Pliny, an authority whom Browne himself is inclined to scout. " ... they are eleven," he has Strabo say, "and four besides."[256] Pliny had said, "There be 11 of them [mouths] in all, over and besides foure more."[257] The parallel in wording here is too close to leave any doubt that Browne's notes had become mixed and that he is ascribing to the gander what was meant for the goose.[258]

---

252 *Works*, III, 247.
253 *Herodoti Halicarnassei historiae lib. IX* ([Geneva], 1566), p. 42.
254 *Works*, III, 247.
255 *Strabonis geographia* (no pagination; Rome, no date), Bk. XVII, one and three-fourths pages from beginning; *The Geography of Strabo*, trans. Hamilton and Falconer, 3 vols. (London, 1889-93), III, 223.
256 *Works*, III, 247.
257 *Naturall Historie or The Historie of the World*, trans. Philemon Holland, 2 vols. in one (London, 1601), I, 99. In the Latin version: "xi. enim reperiuntur, superque quatuor." *Historia mundi naturalis*, 3 vols. in one (Frankfurt, 1582), I, 61.
258 Wilkin at this point has repeated an obvious misprint without com-

Having reached his climax, he now swiftly winds up his argument from the great who were of old with mention of Ptolemy's naming of nine mouths. With one exception[259] he quite accurately reproduces those nine and just as accurately maintains that "there are no less than three different names from those delivered by Pliny."[260] He then states his conclusion in the words of a modern, G. A. Magini: " . . . *de Ostiorum Nili numero et nominibus, valde antiqui Scriptores discordant.*"[261]

This makes for him an easy transition to the modern authorities,[262] of whom he at once mentions three besides Magini. And, when we come to consult Magini, we find tucked away in his geography much of the information Browne has been using and still more that he is going to use:

Nam alii ponunt septem . . . Recentiores tamen tria, vel quatuor tantum ea hodie esse affirmant, ut Guilielmus Tyrius, Petrus Bellonius, testes fide digni, et oculati, atque etiam alii.[263]

Browne, it will be observed, follows quite closely:

. . . as Maginus and others observe, there are now but three or four mouths thereof; as Gulielmus Tyrius long ago, and Bellonius since, both ocular enquirers, with others have attested.[264]

---

ment. Browne refers (III, 247) to "seven and most considerable" mouths and then, apparently, names eight. "Selenneticum" and "Sebenneticum" are clearly the same. Sayle repeats the error in his edition and so does Keynes.
[259] Browne has "Pathmeticum" for "Pathiniticum." *Works*, III, 247. See *Joannis Antonii Magini . . . Geographiae, tum veteris, tum novae* (Arnheim, 1617), third map of Africa. Naturally there are changes in spelling.
[260] *Works*, III, 247-248. Pliny fails to mention Pineptum and Diolcos, and he has "Canopico," missing in Ptolemy's list. But, as the note explains, "Heracleoticum ostium idem esse cum Canopico, notum est ex Ptolemaeo." *Historia mundi naturalis*, 3 vols. in one (Frankfurt, 1582), I, 61.
[261] *Works*, III, 248. The quotation is perfectly accurate. See Magini, *Geographiae universae tum veteris, tum novae absolutissimum opus* (Cologne, 1597), fol. 205. The transition here to the moderns was a natural one because Magini was Ptolemy's continuator.
[262] There were plenty of moderns who still vouched for the traditional seven mouths. Joachim von Watt, *Epitome trium terrae partium, Asiae, Africae et Europae* (Zürich, 1548), D 2, shows the seven in his map of Africa, and explains, "septem enim ostiis grandibus effunditur" (p. 154). J. Honterus, *Rudimenta cosmographica* (Zürich, 1546), Pt. II, d 2, similarly shows seven mouths.
[263] Magini, *Geographiae universae tum veteris, tum novae absolutissimum opus* (Cologne, 1597), fol. 205.
[264] *Works*, III, 248. Among the "others," Henry Blount: "Nile had of old seven streames . . . there now remaine onely three." *A Voyage into the Levant, . . .* (London, 1638), p. 57.

This business of offhand mention of a string of authorities as though they were his discovery, whereas most of them are included in his first source, is, as we have seen, perfectly typical of Browne. There is no great harm in the practice, particularly since he was often sent for supplementary details to the books mentioned in a primary source. Thus, a little below he quotes from the learned Gulielmus, Archbishop of Tyre:

"We wonder much at the ancients, who assigned seven mouths unto Nilus, which we can no otherwise salve than that by process of time, the face of places is altered, and the river hath lost his channels, or that our forefathers did never obtain a true account thereof."

The passage in Gulielmus from which Browne took this is as follows:

Quaerentibus sanè nobis et investigantibus diligenter, nulla alia amnis huius occurrunt hostia: unde miramur plurimum, antiquos Nilum septemfluum dixisse, quasi septem ostiis mare ingrediatur. Nec aliud nobis pro solutione occurrit, nisi aut serie seculorum antiquissima locorum faciem alteratam, fluviumque, sicut aliis etiam amnibus solet crebrius accidere, alveum mutasse: aut pristinae aetatis viros, rei veritatem non esse assecutos.[265]

To have been perfectly accurate, Browne had better have consulted Pierre Belon also, because that author does not say quite what Maginus made him say. His actual statement is as follows: "Qu'il n'y a que deux Grandes Bouches du Nil navigables, ou les grands vaisseaux ronds puissent entrer."[266] And a little further on: "Ces deux eaux [Damietta and Rosetta] sont les plus grands courants du Nil."[267] It is hardly fair, on the basis of these statements, for Browne or Magini to say that Belon restricts the Nile's mouths to three or four.

A contemporary, George Sandys, is now called on for his testimony, and Browne's procedure is here so typical in reproducing the material virtually in the words of his source that I must quote both passages at length. Browne says:

For below Cairo, the river divides itself into four branches, whereof two make the chief and navigable streams, the one running to Pelusium of the

---

[265] *Belli sacri historia* (Basel, no date), p. 475. Just before, Gulielmus has mentioned *four* branches of the Nile.
[266] *Les Observations* (Paris, 1553), fol. 92 verso.
[267] *Ibid.*, fol. 93.

ancients, and now Damietta; the other unto Canopium, and now Rosetta; the other two, saith Mr. Sandys, do run between these, but poor in water.[268]

And Sandys:

Foure miles below Cairo, it devideth into two maine and navigable branches: that next the East running into the Mid-land Sea by Damiata (heretofore Pelusium:) the other inclining unto the West, and formerly called Canopus, falleth into the selfe-same Sea a little below Rosetta. . . . Two other branches there be that runne betweene these, but poore in waters.[269]

Having now adduced his imposing list of scholars, ancient and modern, Browne brings forward the Bible, somewhat with the air of finality. A passage from Holy Scripture itself, he says, has been used to support the claim that the Nile had seven mouths. And, indeed (at least this is the impression given), if it could be proved that Isaiah had the Nile in mind in this passage, there would be no cause for further argument. But reason and a learned commentator, as Browne points out, indicate that the "seven streams" referred to by the prophet may be parts rather of the Euphrates. The passage in *Pseudodoxia* reads:

. . . from the bare name river [found in the Isaiah passage], emphatically signifying Euphrates, and thereby the division of the Assyrian empire into many fractions, which might facilitate their return; as Grotius hath observed . . .[270]

One wonders where he gets the assurance to use so strong a word as "emphatically" unless, indeed, it be from Hugo Grotius' learned note:

Imo in septem rivos dividet Euphratem, id est, imperium Assyriorum in plurimas partes. Medi enim ab Assyriis Chaldaei a Medis defecerunt. Ita gentes illae Hebraeis infestissimae domesticis diffidiis impeditae faciles apud se exsulantibus reditus dedere, quod sequetur.[271]

Next he cites two other Biblical passages, one from Revelation and the second from the apocryphal book of II Esdras, neither of which contributes essentially to his proof.

---

[268] *Works*, III, 248.
[269] *A Relation of a Journey* (2nd ed.; London, 1621), p. 94.
[270] *Works*, III, 249.
[271] *Hugonis Grotii opera omnia theologica*, 4 vols. (London, 1679). Grotius' note to Isaiah 11:15: "Et percutiet eum in septem rivis."

As for maps, they
afford us no assurance or constant description therein. For whereas
Ptolemy[272] hath set forth nine, Hondius[273] in his map of Africa, makes
but eight, and in that of Europe ten; Ortelius,[274] in the map of the Turkish
empire, setteth down eight, in that of Egypt eleven, and Maginus,[275] in his
map of that country, hath observed the same number.[276]

This information is all quite accurately set forth. No books in
Sir Thomas' library, it is safe to say, were better thumbed than
his maps.

Browne now passes to his second popular error, that "the same
river is also accounted the greatest of the earth, called therefore
Fluviorum pater, and *totius Orbis maximus*, by Ortelius."[277] In
establishing his refutation, he shows a broad knowledge of geographers who elevate other rivers into first place, and then proceeds to show cause for the error. The Ancients, he says, magni-
fied the Nile's size because they had never discovered its head, "as
things unknown seem greater than they are."[278] And this, he
adds, is closely associated with the more general human tendency
to convert the great into the greatest. This tendency, he points
out, has its exemplifications on every hand. The Latins considered Rome the greatest city, "but time and geography inform us
that Cairo is bigger, and Quinsay, in China, far exceedeth
both."[279] The same may be said about mountains. And even

---

272 *Joannis Antonii Magini ... Geographiae, tum veteris, tum novae* (Arnheim, 1617), third map of Africa.
273 G. Mercator and J. Hondius, *Atlas; or, a Geographicke Description of
the Regions, Countries and Kingdomes of the World*, 2 vols. (Amsterdam,
1636-38), II, map of Africa, following p. 425; I, map of Europe, following p. 41.
274 Abraham Ortelius, *Theatrum orbis terrarum* (Antwerp, 1612), map of
Turkey, p. 113; map of Egypt, p. 115.
275 G. A. Magini, *Geographiae universae tum veteris, tum novae absolutissimum opus* (Cologne, 1597), fol. 202 verso.
276 *Works*, III, 249.
277 *Works*, III, 250. Hiob Ludolf, *Historia Aethiopica* (Frankfurt, 1681),
Bk. I, pp. 8, 4, agrees: "At Nilus ... caetera Orbis flumina antecellit."
278 *Works*, III, 251.
279 *Ibid.* George Sandys says: " ... than Cairo no Citie can be more
populous." *George Sandys His Travels* (7th ed.; London, 1673), p. 125.
Polo has: " ... the whole city [of Kin-sai] must have contained one million
six hundred thousand families." *Travels of Marco Polo* (London, 1907),
p. 309.

birds. For whereas we have been accustomed to think of the wren as the tiniest of birds, "the discoveries of America" have revealed one far smaller, "the humbird, not much exceeding a beetle."[280]

This is the skeleton of his argument about the second fallacy, which he fills in, intercostally so to speak, with innumerable allusions. In the first place, he says, the Niger exceeds the Nile

about ten degrees in length, that is, no less than six hundred miles. For arising beyond the equator it maketh northward almost 15 degrees, and deflecting after westward, without meanders, continueth a straight course about 40 degrees, and at length with many great currents disburdeneth itself into the occidental ocean.[281]

Every one of these details can be found verified in an atlas like Abraham Ortelius'.[282] Arrianus, in his history of Alexander, Browne says, awards first place to the Ganges.[283] The passage from Arrianus that he has in mind is as follows:

Flumina tot sunt in Indiâ, quot in reliquâ Asiâ: in his maximi sunt Ganges, et Indus . . . uterque et Nilo Aegyptis et Istro Scythico (etiamsi in unum alveum confluerent) major est.[284]

Pointing out that Baptista Scortia contends for "the river of Plate in America," Browne continues:

---

[280] *Works*, III, 251. Sir Thomas has perhaps taken this bit from Samuel Purchas, or rather Fernandez de Oviedo whom Purchas translates: "There are found in the firme land certaine birds, so little, that the whole bodie of one of them is no bigger then the top of the biggest finger of a mans hand . . . This Bird, beside her littlenesse, is of such velositie and swiftnesse in flying, that who so seeth her flying in the aire, cannot see her flap or beate her wings after any other sort then doe the Dorres, or humble Bees, or Beetels, . . ." *Purchas His Pilgrimes*, 20 vols. (Glasgow, 1905-07), XV, 168.
[281] *Works*, III, 250.
[282] *Theatrum orbis terrarum* (Antwerp, 1612), map of Africa, p. 4. The Niger is represented there to be just over ten degrees longer than the Nile.
[283] *Works*, III, 250. Browne may have derived this knowledge from Girolamo Cardano. Cf.: *Hieronymi Cardani Mediolanensis medici de subtilitate libri XXI* (Basel, 1553), p. 93: "Maximus enim fluviorum, ut Arrianus scribit, Ganges." Cf. *The Geography of Strabo*, trans. Hamilton and Falconer, 3 vols. (London, 1889-93), III, 96: "For that the Ganges is the largest of known rivers in the three continents, it is generally agreed; next to this is the Indus; and, thirdly, the Danube; and, fourthly, the Nile."
[284] *Arriani De expedit. Alex. Magni historiarum libri VII* (Amsterdam, 1668), I, 514.

for that, as Maffeus hath delivered, falleth into the ocean in the latitude of forty leagues, and with that force and plenty, that men at sea do taste fresh water before they approach so near as to discover the land.[285]

It looks as if Browne might have got these details direct from Maffei, but they come, as a fact, whole-cloth from Scortia:

Vincitur denique, ut taceam de Zaire, de quo diximus in fine c. 2 ab Argenteo fluvio in eadem America, qui ostio patente ad quadraginta leucas adeo violentus currit in Oceanum, ut nautae priusquam tellurem ex alto conspiciant, dulces latices hauriant; ut scripsit Joannes Petrus Maffeus lib. 2. historiarum Indicarum.[286]

Girolamo Cardano, Browne says, prefers the Orellana (the Amazon).[287] This is possibly another place where Sir Thomas' notes have got mixed because Cardano makes the statement, "Maximus enim fluviorum, ut Arrianus scribit, Ganges."[288] Browne would seem here to have confused Cardano with Magini, who, he says, has reported that the Orellana "hath been navigated 6000 miles, and opens in a channels [*sic*] of ninety leagues broad."[289] The passage in Magini reads:

Maragnon quoque fluvius in immensam latitudinem ac longitudinem patescit; ferunt enim navigatum fuisse sex millibus milliaribus, ac eius ostium 70. leucas complecti.[290]

Browne's final reference is quite typical since he implies it is conclusive because the authority cited, Acosta, was "an ocular witness." "They that sail in the middle [of the Orellana] can make no land on either side,"[291] he has Acosta say. Unfortunately for his point, the latter's evidence is not based on his personal observation:

---

285 *Works*, III, 250.

286 *De natura et incremento Nili* (London, 1617), p. 33. Scortia has quoted Maffei accurately. Cf. *Jo. Petri Maffeii Bergomatis ... Opera omnia Latine scripta*, 2 vols. (Bergamo, 1747), I, 40-41. The reference is properly given to *Historiarum indicarum*, Bk. II.

287 *Works*, III, 250.

288 *Hieronymi Cardani Mediolanensis medici de subtilitate libri XXI* (Basel, 1553), p. 93.

289 *Works*, III, 250.

290 *Geographiae universae tum veteris, tum novae absolutissimum opus* (Cologne, 1597), fol. 283. For the discrepancy between Browne's "ninety" and Magini's "70," see p. 143 *supra*.

291 *Works*, III, 250.

That great floud called by some the river of Amazons, by others Marañon, and by some the river of Orellana, . . . ought to blemish all the rest . . . And that which seemes incredible, when you saile through the midst of it, you shall see nothing but aire and water. . . . We have learned from credible persons the great and wonderfull bredth of this river (which, in my opinion, deserves well the name of Empresse and Queene of all flouds), which was by the report of a brother of our company, who, being then yong, sailed it in the company of Pedro de Ursua.[292]

In the course of impressing us with the enormous size of *other* rivers, he tosses in a detail belittling the Nile—that it is so narrow in at least one place that the Tartar horsemen of Selimus could swim across it from Cairo to meet the forces of Tonumbeus. This circumstance, lifted from Richard Knolles's *Generall Historie*,[293] is particularly significant because it is found in an exciting account of a fight between the two forces mentioned, an account that seems to have engaged Browne's attention principally because it contains the incidental detail implying the Nile's narrowness.[294]

The third popular error with which he deals concerns the Nile's yearly overflow and the date of its inception. Some people, he says, think the annual overflow is peculiar to the Nile whereas plenty of other rivers flood each year.[295] In explaining the erroneous belief, he notes that it is a common error to transform a remarkable quality into a unique one, and that writers have done this not only with the Nile's overflow but with snakes in Ireland, the volcano on Etna, and crocodiles on the Nile.[296]

Some, he notes, have even gone so far as to contend that the inundations begin on a fixed day. Here, he thinks, we have a case of the moderns' interpreting the Ancients too literally. If the day had been fixed, it would have been impossible for the devil

---

[292] Father Joseph de Acosta, *The Natural and Moral History of the Indies.* Reprinted for Hakluyt Society from translation of Edward Grimston (1604), ed. C. R. Markham, 2 vols. (London, 1880), I, 82.

[293] 3rd ed.; London, 1621, p. 549.

[294] Cf. pp. 135-136 *supra.*

[295] *Works*, III, 252.

[296] *Works*, III, 253-254. "Thus crocodiles were thought to be peculiar unto Nile, and the opinion so possessed Alexander, that when he had discovered some in Ganges, he fell upon a conceit he had found the head of Nilus . . . " P. 254. Cf.: "When Alexander saw crocodiles in the Hydaspes . . . he thought that he had discovered the sources of the Nile." *The Geography of Strabo*, trans. Hamilton and Falconer, 3 vols. (London, 1889-93), III, 88.

to gain prestige with the Egyptians by predicting just when the flood would begin! Lastly, he insists, we must appeal to common sense; nothing that depends, as the Nile does, on conditions of weather can be absolutely regular. In short, we tend to fall into the mistake of setting exact limits to things whose bounds are flexible, as we do with the period of adolescence, with the duration of puppies' blindness; even the computation of 365 days to the year is not precisely accurate.

The manner of his building up and filling in his argument with respect to the Nile's annual overflow is like that with respect to the river's size. Regular overflow is not peculiar to the Nile for it happens to the Niger and Zaire, the Suama and Spirito Santo as well as the Indian Menan and Livonian Dvina.[297] And the Bible speaks of the inundations of Jordan "in the time of harvest."[298] Diodorus, Seneca, and Strabo hit on the proper cause of the overflow, the rains in Ethiopia. Browne's lumping of authorities here spells trouble, as it so often does. It is quite true that Diodorus[299] and Strabo[300] are on record as favoring this explanation for the overflow; but Seneca directly opposes it:

Anaxagoras ait ex Aethiopie iugis solutas nives ad Nilum usque decurrere. In eadem opinione omnis vetustas fuit . . . Sed falsum esse argumentis plurimis patet.[301]

And his arguments against the theory follow at some length. Obviously it is Anaxagoras who contends for the theory and Browne, finding it set forth in Seneca, hastily jotted the latter's name down into his commonplace book without reading Seneca's refutation.

---

[297] *Works*, III, 252. For this last, Browne gives as authority Giovanni Botero. I have searched in vain for the mention of this river in Botero's *Della ragion di stato* ... (Ferrara, 1589) and in his longer work, *Relations of the Most Famous Kingdomes and Common-wealthes Throughout the World* (London, 1630).

[298] *Works*, III, 252.

[299] "And that therefore it is no wonder if the mountainous parts of Ethiopia, which lies much higher than Egypt, are soaked with continual rains, wherewith the river being filled, overflows." *The Historical Library of Diodorus the Sicilian*, 2 vols. (London, 1814), I, 47.

[300] "Persons in later times learnt by experience as eye-witnesses, that the Nile owes its rise to summer rains, which fall in great abundance in Upper Ethiopia." *The Geography of Strabo*, trans. Hamilton and Falconer, 3 vols. (London, 1889-93), III, 224.

[301] *Opera* (Basel, 1529), p. 452.

The explanation, Browne continues, has since been substantiated by moderns such as Francisco Alvares and Antonius Ferdinandus, both eyewitnesses. The former, he says, has "left a description of Ethiopia, affirming that from the middle of June unto September, there fell in this time continual rains."[302] The passage Browne has in mind occurs in Francisco Alvares' *Viaggio fatto nella Etiopia*:

La causa che il Nilo inonda l'Egitto, è questa, che cominciando, 'l verno generale nell' Ethiopia alla meta di Giugno fino à mezo Settembre, per le grandissime pioggie, che di continuo senza cessar si fanno in quel tempo, il Nilo si fa grosso & inonda l'Egitto.[303]

As for the ridiculous assumption that the Nile begins to increase on a fixed day, June 17,[304] he says, not even the credulous Ancients believed that, "Herodotus, Diodorus, Seneca, &c. delivering only that it happeneth about the entrance of the sun into Cancer."[305] What Herodotus actually says is that "the Nile comes down increasing in volume from the summer solstice onwards for a hundred days."[306] And Diodorus says practically the same thing: "The Nile begins to swell at the time of the summer solstice."[307] Browne had in mind the following passage from Seneca: "At Nilus ante ortum caniculae auget mediis aestibus, ultra aequinoctium."[308] Sir Thomas goes on then to give other examples of the Ancients' conservatism in matters of time, Hippocrates employing the flexible "Sub Cane et ante Canem," and Aristotle[309] constantly resorting to the modifiers *circa* and *magna*

---

302 *Works*, III, 253.
303 *Delle navigationi et viaggi nel qual si contiene la descrittione dell' Africa* (Venice, 1550), fol. 273 verso. *Del viaggio fatto nella Etiopia per don Francesco Alvarez* begins in *Primo volume*, fol. 204.
304 Leo's translator, John Pory, held this belief. Leo Africanus, *History and Description of Africa*, 3 vols. (Hakluyt Soc.; London, 1896), I, 17: "Nilus ... continueth in his yeerely increase fortie daies, and forty daies in decrease; to wit, from the seventeenth of June to the sixt of October." This Pory practically repeats from Leo himself. *Ibid.*, III, 936.
305 *Works*, III, 254.
306 *History*, trans. G. C. Macaulay, 2 vols. (London, 1914), I, 124.
307 *The Historical Library of Diodorus the Sicilian*, 2 vols. (London, 1814), I, 45. On the previous page, Diodorus says: "... it is not so strange for the Nile about summer time to increase."
308 *Opera* (Basel, 1529), p. 451.
309 Cf. *Works of Aristotle*, ed. J. A. Smith and W. D. Ross, 12 vols. (Oxford, 1908-52), IV, 547a: "about the rising of the dog-star"; 569a: "about

ex parte.[310] Browne then notes that Scaliger, translating a passage from Aristotle, differs from Theodorus, who has rendered the Greek into "ante Nonas," making it "Junii initio" and thus saving the Stagirite from setting a definite day: "For affirming it happeneth before the Nones, he alloweth but one day, that is, the Calends; for in the Roman account, the second day is the fourth of the Nones of June."[311]

A further argument against the fixed-day belief is that, were there a set day, the devil could have gained no credit for predicting that day; and yet "when he perceived the rains to fall in Ethiopia, [he] would presage unto the Egyptians the day of its inundation."[312] This rare bit is taken from St. Athanasius' life of St. Anthony:

So, too, with respect to the water of the river, they [demons] sometimes make foolish statements. For having seen that there has been much rain in the regions of Ethiopia, and knowing that they are the cause of the flood of the river, before the water has come to Egypt they run on and announce it. And this men could have told, if they had as great power of running as the demons.[313]

So variable, indeed, is the overflow that in "some years," Browne says, "there hath been no increase at all, as some conceive in the years of famine under Pharaoh; as Seneca and divers relate of the eleventh year of Cleopatra."[314] This last is taken quite accurately from Seneca's statement: "Biennio continuo, regnante Cleopatra, non ascendisse decimo regni anno et undecimo constat."[315] Browne then adds: "nor [for] nine years to-

---

the rising of the Dog-star"; 599[a]: "about thirty days at the rising of the Dog-star"; also 602[a] and 633[a].

310 *Works*, III, 254.

311 *Ibid.* The passage in Theodorus is to be found in *Aristoteles De animalibus. In hoc presenti volumine infra scripta habentur Aristotelis opuscula a Theodoro Gaza de Greco in Latinum iampridem* (?) *versa* (?) (1525), fol. 22. Scaliger's translation is in *Aristotelis Historia de animalibus; Iulio Caesare Scaligero interprete, cum eiusdem commentarijs* (Toulouse, 1619), p. 712: "Thunni, scombrique coëunt mense Februario post Idus: pariunt Junii initio."

312 *Works*, III, 254-255.

313 In *A Select Library of the Nicene and Post-Nicene Fathers of the Christian Church*, 2nd Ser., ed. Philip Schaff and Henry Wace, 14 vols. (New York, 1890-1900), IV, 205.

314 *Works*, III, 255.

315 *Opera* (Basel, 1529), p. 452.

gether, as is testified by Calisthenes." We may well be surprised that Callisthenes should be brought in here. His presence is probably due to a slip by Browne. Following a practice fairly common with him, he has probably read on in his original source and found an extra bit of evidence to support his contention. This is in a later passage from Seneca: "Per novem annos, non ascendisse Nilum superioribus seculis *Callimachus* est autor."[316] Here obviously is the source of Browne's "nine years together." But somehow, possibly through wretched handwriting in the commonplace books, Callimachus has got himself transmogrified into Callisthenes.

Some years it hath also retarded, and come far later than usually it was expected, as according to Sozomen and Nicephorus it happened in the days of Theodosius; whereat the people were ready to mutiny, because they might not sacrifice unto the river, according to the custom of their predecessors.[317]

He has taken this mainly from Sozomen:

Quo quidem tempore, aiunt Aegypti fluvium tardius solito exundare coepisse. Indignabantur ergo Aegyptii, quod fluvio ex more institutoque majorum sacrificare haudquaquam permitterentur.[318]

The fourth vulgar error concerns rather Egypt than the Nile, that "it never raineth" there, "the river supplying that defect."[319] But there is the ocular testimony, not of one but three bold men and true, that it does rain, and rather plentifully, at such places as Cairo, Alexandria, and Damietta. Furthermore, and here again is the clinching argument, does not Holy Scripture state, "Behold I will cause it to rain a very great hail, such as hath not been in Egypt since the foundation thereof, even until now."[320] Browne's explanation for this mistake is like the others, the human tendency to superlativize a comparative; because it rains seldom, to say it rains never, just as we erroneously aver that the

---

[316] *Ibid.* Italics mine.
[317] *Works*, III, 255.
[318] *Socratis scholastici et Hermiae Sozomeni Historia ecclesiastica* (Mainz, 1677), II, 736.
[319] *Works*, III, 256.
[320] *Works*, III, 257.

sun shines every day in Rhodes, that the chameleon never eats, and that eight-month babies cannot live, whereas Aristotle maintains the contrary concerning such babies in Egypt.[321]

Browne's "honourable and ocular testimony" was that of Sir William Paston, who, he said, testified that "it rained in grand Cairo divers days together."[322] But, though he knew Paston[323] personally, he seems not to have taken the statement from his lips but rather from John Greaves, whom he mentions as further authority just below: "Whereto we might add the latter testimony of learned Mr. Greaves, in his accurate description of the Pyramids."[324] It is typical of Browne that this sentence should have been added in the second edition of Pseudodoxia; he was forever supplementing his chapters with additional data gleaned from new publications.[325] It was his way of keeping up-to-date. John Greaves's full statement is as follows:

I cannot sufficiently wonder at the Ancients, who generally deny the fall of raine in Aegypt. . . . Whereas for two months, namely December, and January, I have not knowne it raine, so constantly and with so much violence, at London, as I found it to do at Alexandria . . . And not onely there, but also at Grand Cairo, my very noble, and worthy Friend Sir William Paston, at the same time observed, that there fell much raine.[326]

A third authority whom Browne adduces is Prosper Alpinus, "who lived long in that country": "Cayri rarò decidunt pluviae; Alexandriae, Pelusiique et in omnibus locis mari adjacentibus, pluit largissime et saepe; that is, it raineth seldom at Cairo, but at Alexandria, Damietta, and places near the sea, it raineth plentifully and often."[327] And Alpinus is quoted again below: "The

---

321 Works, III, 257-258. Cf.: "In these places [Egypt, among others] the eight-months' children live and are brought up." Works of Aristotle, ed. J. A. Smith and W. D. Ross, 12 vols. (Oxford, 1908-52), IV, 584b.
322 Works, III, 256.
323 He was the father of Sir Robert Paston, Browne's particular friend.
324 Works, III, 257.
325 Greaves's book was published in 1646, the very year of the first edition of Pseudodoxia. For the interesting changes made in new editions, see unpublished thesis of T. M. Westfall, "Sir Thomas Browne's Revisions in Pseudodoxia Epidemica: A Study in the Development of His Mind" (Princeton, 1939).
326 Pyramidographia (London, 1646), pp. 74-75, n.
327 Works, III, 256-257. The passage is taken from Alpinus' De medicina Aegyptiorum (Paris, 1645), fol. 11 verso.

same concerning hail is inferrible from Prosper Alpinus, *Rarissimè nix, grando*, it seldom snoweth or haileth . . ."[328]

It has been noted above[329] that the chapter on the Nile ends with what appears to be an afterthought. The error just discussed, that it does not rain in Egypt, concerned the Nile only indirectly in that it arose from assuming that the river made up for the absence of rain. And now the last point[330] is still more tenuously connected with the Nile; it has to do with past attempts to dig a canal between the Mediterranean and the Red Sea or, as Browne believes more likely, between the Nile and the Red Sea. Browne traces attempts to connect the Nile and the Red Sea through Sesostris and Darius to Philadelphus. And, since the latter was partially successful, he says, we should not ascribe to such an undertaking the proverb "to cut an isthmus," meaning to take great pains and effect nothing, but rather attribute it to the futile attempts of the Cnidians or to the equally futile efforts to cut the isthmus of Corinth. This consideration then leads him to descant on Apollo's order to the Cnidians that they should desist because, if god had intended their peninsula to be an island, he would have made it that way to begin with. Sir Thomas then brings his saving common sense to bear in refuting such reasoning since learned men have shown that nature, "the art of God," has created islands where there were none originally and that many have been "made since by art." And this, finally, brings him to his very practical suggestion, a plea for the digging of the Panama Canal.[331] Thus, a chapter that begins firmly with a well-formulated introduction, followed by three arguments carefully constructed, tapers off into a fourth discussion that is only remotely germane to the subject and a fifth that has virtually nothing to do with it at all.

How characteristic all this is of Sir Thomas Browne is easily recognized by anyone who is at all familiar with him and his work. He seems to have made up his mind, in the composition of *Pseudodoxia*, that he will follow through a consistently developed argument. But his tendency to saunter down a bypath

---

[328] *Works*, III, 257. From Alpinus, *loc. cit.*
[329] Page 150.
[330] *Works*, III, 258.
[331] *Works*, III, 259.

is occasionally insuperable. He loved, as he says, to lose himself in a mystery, to pursue his reason to an *O altitudo!* The Browne of *Religio medici* might be exorcized, but he was far from dead.

That he was acutely conscious of having in hand a type of writing new to him is manifest on nearly every page of *Pseudodoxia*. By way of reaction he had willed for himself a task of a comparatively substantial nature wherein imagination should inspire science and science should temper imagination. That the project was not to be an outstanding success, he himself would have predicted. But, in the very awareness of certain tendencies that partially unfitted him, he set about to overcome those tendencies. His commonplace books are evidence of the intention. *Pseudodoxia* is, in the main, a quite serious piece of work, designed to blast countless theories stubbornly adhered to; and for that purpose buttressed with innumerable exempla drawn from wide reading. The subject matter may have been at times uncongenial to the author in that it involved often mere citation of authorities. But it was like him, having undertaken what he knew to be an important work, to carry forward with all of his inexhaustible curiosity and energy. The result is a book that clearly had its impact upon the minds of the seventeenth century.